...nal Gallery

...tian
...nteenth
...ury
...ting

...n from collections
...in Britain and Ireland

... November 1979

...oman Potterton

Published by Order of the Trustees
Publications Department, National Gallery
London, 1979

Note on the Arrangement of the Catalogue

The pictures are catalogued and exhibited approximately in chronological sequence of execution as far as this can be established.

In the case of each picture as full a provenance as it was reasonably possible to obtain has been attempted.

The usual practice of listing separately some or all of the literature on a painting, relevant and irrelevant, has not been followed, and pertinent references are given within the body of the texts. They are abbreviated to author or key name and date; full information will be found in the Bibliography (p.156).

In the case of artists' biographies references to basic works only are given separately at the foot of each entry. Versions of compositions are listed as completely as possible and, if they have been illustrated, this reference is sometimes given. Exceptions are for example Strozzi's *Concert* (No.23) where it seemed silly to list photographic references for all the very numerous versions and copies. Sizes of versions are also included where they seem relevant, e.g. Turchi (No.5).

There is a full account of previous exhibitions in which pictures have been shown, and engravings after exhibited pictures and preparatory drawings for them are cited where they are known.

Designed by James Shurmer

Edited by Emily Lane

ISBN 0 901791 67 9

Contents

Front and back covers:
Bernardo Strozzi
Personifications of Summer and Spring
Catalogue No.26 (details)

Page 4
A Personification of Venice, detail of an
engraving from J. von Sandrart's
Academia Nobilissimae Artis Pictoriae
(1683)

Page 6
Detail of Carpioni No.39

Foreword

This exhibition is, I believe, the first to be held in England on the theme of Venetian seventeenth-century painting. The fame and popularity in this country of painting in Venice in the preceding and subsequent centuries have more than overshadowed activity there in the intervening years; and a vaguely anthropo-morphic-cum-seasonal view of art as a process of burgeoning, withering and re-flowering has assigned to the Venetian seventeenth century the role of a wintry age, marking time between the death of Tintoretto and the birth of Tiepolo.

How little this accords with the facts is demonstrated by the present exhibition. Some of the painters working in Venice during the period are great in their own right, and not merely as successors or precursors of other men. Such artists as Fetti, Strozzi and Liss may be comparatively unfamiliar, but their pictures are at once original enough and attractive enough to make us take note of them. Other artists have passed into a deeper penumbra still, yet they too are seen here to possess individuality and the capacity to surprise and impress the spectator.

It was from the first inherent in the concept of this exhibition that it should draw mainly on British collections – if only as a reminder, well brought out in Homan Potterton's Introduction, of how early some leading collectors in this country owned Venetian seventeenth-century pictures.

We are greatly indebted to the generosity of all the lenders, headed by Her Majesty the Queen, who have made this exhibition possible. The exhibition has been devised, organised and catalogued by my colleague Homan Potterton with as much enthusiasm as scholarship, and I am grateful to him for an event that has proved truly enlightening.

On his and the Gallery's behalf, I must record our thanks for the design of the exhibition to Christopher Nell and Ian McDonald, of the Department of the Environment, and to James Shurmer both for the graphics and the catalogue lay-out. Homan Potterton, who has acknowledged in the text those who in particular instances have given him information, wishes to express his gratitude for their kindness and interest to Robert and Bertina Suida Manning, Mary Newcome Schleier, Nicholas Turner, Michael Wynne and, in Venice, Professor Rodolfo Pallucchini, Sonia Finzi Pasquali, Stefania Mason Rinaldi and Sylvano De Tuoni. Also to Emily Lane for her careful editing of the text; and in the National Gallery to Sheila Waller for her painstaking typing of it, and, for patience and help, to Margaret Cooke, Elspeth Hector, Angelina Morhange and Margaret Stewart.

Exhibitions like this place a considerable burden on nearly all the staff and resources of the Gallery; I gratefully acknowledge that contribution.

The modest price of this catalogue has been made possible by the Publications Committee of the Trustees, which decided, in the interests of scholarship and in the hope of fostering wider artistic appreciation generally, to allot a considerable sum from Publications Department funds to subsidise it. For this decision we are most grateful to the Trustees.

Michael Levey, *Director*

Introduction

There can be few great collections where the unfamiliarity of Venetian seventeenth-century painting is more pointedly highlighted than in the National Gallery itself. Paintings from the sixteenth century by Giovanni Bellini, Titian, Veronese and Tintoretto are among the greatest works in the collection, and a ravishing ceiling painting by Giovanni Battista Tiepolo is one of the principal masterpieces of the eighteenth century in the Gallery. Tintoretto, the last of the great Venetian painters of the Cinquecento, died in 1594 and Tiepolo was not born until over a hundred years later, in 1696. From the intervening years the Gallery is able to contribute to the present exhibition only five paintings which are truly of the seventeenth century. Of these only two, *Jacob reproaching Laban* by Carlo Saraceni [*No.2*] and *An Old Man holding a Pilgrim Bottle* ascribed to Pietro Bellotti [*No.48*] are by Venetian artists; two others are by German painters who worked in Venice, Johann Carl Loth [*No.43*] and Johann Liss [*No.17*], and the fifth, *A Personification of Fame* [*No.25*], is by a Genoese-born artist, Bernardo Strozzi. None of these pictures entered the collection before 1920. Between them they illustrate one important point: the contribution made by non-Venetian artists to the development of painting in Venice in the seventeenth century.

Strozzi's *Fame,* in its colour and technique, is perhaps more sumptuously beautiful than any other Italian seventeenth-century picture in the National Gallery, and it serves well to introduce a school of painting of which it is typical and to which its painter contributed much. It is pertinent that *Fame* seems to inquire of us which of her two trumpets, representing the dual aspects of her character, worthy and unworthy, she should sound as a keynote to Venetian seventeenth-century painting.

Strozzi's Fame might also be a personification of the Republic of Venice itself in the seventeenth century – seductively attractive and anxious to please, although at the same time slightly unsure and nervous. Once a great and wealthy republic with extensive colonies in the Eastern Mediterranean, and geographically in a position to exploit her role as a rich centre of international trade, Venice had by the seventeenth century become accustomed to adversity and decline. From 1453, when Constantinople fell to the Ottoman Turks, she gradually lost most of her Eastern colonies, and after the rounding of the Cape of Good Hope in 1478 she could no longer monopolise with profit commercial traffic between East and West. Under constant threat from the Turks, and envied because of her power by her mainland neighbours, not least the Papal States (the League of Cambrai was formed in 1508 for the partition of Venetian territories), Venice was challenged further in the seventeenth century by the ambitions in Italy of the Spanish-Austrian Habsburgs. In 1606 came the Papal Interdict: Venice, attempting to defend the absolute authority of the State against that of Rome, was excommunicated by Pope Paul V. By this time her sole remaining colony in the Eastern Mediterranean was Crete: after a costly struggle that lasted twenty-five years, she lost that to the Turks in 1669. War against the same foes in the 1680s and 1690s resulted in her regaining the Morea, only to lose it again by the terms of the Peace of Passarowitz, concluded without her knowledge between the Austrians and her enemies in 1718. Such was the undignified ending of the centuries-old struggle between the Republic and the Ottoman Empire, and the beginning of the decline of the Most Serene Republic, the Serenissima.

Painting in seventeenth-century Venice

Venetian art in the seventeenth century is never a long chapter in art history books. Only in architecture, with Baldassare Longhena (1598–1682), did Venice produce an artist of truly international stature, and his church of S. Maria della Salute, built over a period of fifty years from 1631, is a forceful and constant reminder of this. Dominating the entrance to the Grand Canal, it was erected under decree from the Senate and dedicated to the Virgin as thanksgiving for Venice's survival of the plague which swept through the city and the Veneto in 1629–30 (killing, along with many others, the painters Bassetti, Liss and Ottino). Although similar great projects were pursued by painters, their work is eclipsed by the glories of Venetian painting which preceded and succeeded them. Liberi's *Brazen Serpent* (1659) in S. Pietro di Castello, Zanchi's *Plague at Venice* (1666) in S. Rocco, and Fumiani's vast ceiling in the church of S. Pantalon (1684–1704) remain among the least loved of all works of art in Venice.

Most accounts of Venetian Seicento painting describe it as a period of slumber, enlivened only by the contributions made about 1620 by a trio of outsiders, born in the 1580s and 1590s, who came to work (and die) in the city: Domenico Fetti [*Nos.7–15*], Johann Liss [*Nos.16,17*], and Bernardo Strozzi [*Nos.18–27*]. As a result, the importance for Venetian painting of these three artists, whose work is characterised in general by a brilliant use of colour with which the Venetians were anyway familiar, tends to be overstressed at the expense of other painters – in particular the tenebrists Giovanni Battista Langetti [*No.41*], Johann Carl Loth [*Nos.42,43*], and Antonio Zanchi [*Nos.44,45*], born in the 1630s, who contributed much more to the rejuvenation of Venetian painting is the seventeenth century.

It is true that after the great period from the late fifteenth to the end of the sixteenth century the Venetian tradition was exhausted, and more important schools of painting developed from the beginning of the seventeenth century in other centres – Bologna, Naples, and of course Rome. But the Seicento in Venice should not be seen as dormant, for there, perhaps more than in any other city, a cross-fertilisation of a wide variety of different artistic trends produced a lively development in painting that eventually culminated in the work of the eighteenth-century painters Giovanni Battista Piazzetta, Sebastiano Ricci [*No.53*], Giovanni Antonio Pellegrini [*No.54*], and eventually Giovanni Battista Tiepolo. By the seventeenth century Venice was, with Rome, the most visited of all Italian cities, and it was inevitable that an enormous number of artists with widely varying backgrounds should be attracted to the city which contained what were among the greatest masterpieces of the Italian Renaissance. Some of these visiting artists painted in Venice and left, some settled, and most contributed in some way to the melting-pot from which eighteenth-century Venetian painting eventually emerged. Venetian Seicento painting is not best studied within the Salute, although the altarpieces there by the Neapolitan Luca Giordano are of fundamental importance. Instead it is in S. Pietro di Castello, S. Zaccharia and above all in S. Maria del Soccorso at Rovigo in the Veneto, where Maffei, Liberi, Ricchi, della Vecchia, Zanchi, Celesti and others worked, that one can best see the painting of the period.

The historian of Venetian seventeenth-century painting is Marco Boschini (1613–78), himself a painter, engraver and etcher and in his youth a pupil of Palma Giovane. His *La carta del navegar pitoresco,* published in Venice in 1660, is a dialogue in verse form between a Venetian Senator and dilettante and a professor of painting, who, as an *alter ego* of Boschini himself, indoctrinates the Senator in the glories of Venetian painting. Boschini later published a guide to painting in Venice, *Le minere della pittura* (1664), which he amplified in a second edition, *Le ricche minere della pittura* (1674). He knew almost all his contemporaries who were painters, and considered Venetian painting superior to all other schools, a view which his writings serve to propagate.

The continuation of the sixteenth-century tradition

With the deaths of Veronese in 1588 and Tintoretto in 1594, Palma Giovane (*c.*1548–1628), who had trained in the studio of Titian, became the most prominent and prolific painter working in Venice [*No.1*]. In the 'Breve instruzione' (*sic*) with which he prefaces his *Ricche minere* of 1674, Boschini divides the Venetian painters working at the time into 'sette maniere', the first of the seven modes being Palma Giovane, whom Boschini much admired. The other six are Leonardo Corona, Andrea Vicentino, Sante Perando, Antonio Aliense called Il Vasilecchi, Pietro Malombra and Girolamo Pilotti. To Boschini, the work of these painters derived from and continued the tradition of late Titian, Tintoretto and Veronese. Most of the seven were employed in the decoration of the Doge's Palace, in particular the Sale del Maggior Consiglio, del Collegio, del Senato and dello Scrutinio, after the fire of 1577 which destroyed the earlier decorations.

It is on the ceiling of the Sala del Maggior Consiglio that Palma Giovane painted, in 1578–84, as pendant to Veronese's *Apotheosis of Venice,* what is probably his finest work, *Venice crowned by Victory* [*Fig.1*]. Much of Palma's work, consisting of countless altarpieces and other religious canvases for Venetian churches, is dull and, it has to be said, routine, although in work such as the cycle of paintings in the Oratorio dei Crociferi in Venice (begun in 1583) he can show himself as a not altogether unworthy heir to his great predecessors. In the last decades of his life his style, which Boschini characterised as 'in design

Figure 1
Palma Giovane:
*Venice crowned by
Victory,* from the
ceiling of the Sala
del Maggior
Consiglio in the
Doge's Palace,
Venice, 1578–84.

approximating to Tintoretto and in colour to Titian . . . his nudes tightly drawn and in lively postures, his colour mellow, soft, tender and fleshy', changed little. Palma, who worked in a manner that was more Tintorettesque than Boschini's description would imply, dominated the entire generation of painters working in Venice in the last decades of the sixteenth and early years of the seventeenth centuries, including Odoardo Fialetti (b.1576), best known for his portraits of Doges [*Fig.2*], but mentioned as an etcher by his teacher Boschini.

By the time of Palma's death in 1628 at the age of eighty, the tradition of which

Figure 2
Odoardo Fialetti:
*Doge Niccolò Dona
(Donato).* By
gracious permission
of Her Majesty the
Queen.
164.5 × 123.8 cm.

LEONARDO DONATO
DOGE DI VENETIA·

he was the last important exponent had almost expired. The paintings dating from this time in the Doge's Palace illustrate the military and naval triumphs of the Republic in past centuries on the mainland and in the East: conceived as an apotheosis of Venice, these huge canvases were no doubt also intended to be an apotheosis of Venetian painting. Sadly this is not so: hanging alongside the paintings of Tintoretto and Veronese, the works of Palma Giovane, Vicentino, Vasilecchi and others can only show that at that point the genius of Venetian painting, like the power of Venice herself, was exhausted.

The beginnings of renewal in the work of Padovanino

It is to the work of a painter born not in Venice but in Padua, Alessandro Varotari, called Il Padovanino (1588–1648), that one looks for evidence of a renaissance in Venetian painting in the early Seicento. He was brought up in Padua, where he knew and admired the work of Titian's collaborator and imitator, Damiano Mazza (active 1573), and an early visit to Rome, where he copied the bacchanals of Titian, confirmed in him an admiration for that painter which lasted throughout his life [No.4]. By returning to the example of early Titian, particularly with regard to colour, and in seeking a more classical expression of form, fostered by contact in Rome with the Bolognese painters Domenichino, the Carracci and Albani, Padovanino's style was directly opposed to the manneristic sub-Tintoretto paintings of Palma Giovane and his school. Though he was by no means a great painter, Padovanino's ideals were highly important, for they led to a break with the continuing tradition as practised by Palma, and to a renewal in Venetian painting inspired by early Titian. Padovanino was the most important teacher in Venice in the first half of the seventeenth century, and numbered among his pupils almost all the most talented Venetian-born painters of the mid-century. From him, through his pupils and their pupils in turn, can be traced an artistic lineage which leads to the great painters of the eighteenth century.

Caravaggism in the Veneto

The influence of Caravaggio was probably less in Venice than in any other Italian city, and it was a trio of painters from Verona in the Veneto, Pasquale Ottino (1578–1630), Alessandro Turchi (1578–1649) [No.5] and Marcantonio Bassetti (1586–1630) [No.6], who were most drawn to Caravaggism. All worked for a time in Rome, where Bassetti had been sent in 1616 by Palma Giovane to study with Saraceni. Turchi stayed on; Ottino and Bassetti returned to Verona, only to die there in the plague of 1630. Caravaggesque elements are found in the work of all three – in Bassetti's colour, in particular, and in Ottino and Turchi's strongly lit and often nude figures – but none of them can really be called a doctrinaire Caravaggesque, and their influence in the Veneto was in any case relatively slight.

Carlo Saraceni (1579–1620) left Venice in 1598 for Rome, where for a time he became a follower of Caravaggio, and returned only in the last year of his life, when he was summoned to paint in the Sala del Maggior Consiglio of the Doge's Palace the large *Oath of Doge Enrico Dandolo* [Fig.3]. However he almost certainly sent paintings to Venice from Rome, and it is through him and his pupil and collaborator, the Frenchman Jean Le Clerc (c. 1587–1633), who accompanied him in 1620, that Caravaggism was introduced to Venice, albeit with relatively little effect. After Saraceni's death Le Clerc completed his painting for the Sala del Maggior Consiglio, and then left Venice in 1622.

Figure 3 Carlo Saraceni and Jean Le Clerc:
The Oath of Doge Enrico Dandolo, 1620–22. Sala del Maggior Consiglio, Doge's Palace, Venice.

Fetti, Liss, Strozzi and other settlers in Venice

By the time of his first visit to Venice in the summer of 1621, the Roman-born Domenico Fetti (c.1588/89–1623) was already well versed in the language of Venetian painting and had used works by Tintoretto and Veronese as models for some of his own compositions (see his biography, below). Although he only painted in Venice for the last eight months of his life, his pictures were known to Venetian collectors certainly by later in the century (Savini-Branca 1965, *passim*), and it is reasonable to suppose that some of the many versions of his compositions were collected there during his lifetime. His small paintings [Nos.11–15], with their lyrical colour and strong feeling for humanity, must have seemed extraordinary in the Venice of his time, dominated as it was by the grandiose and often mysteriously dark canvases of Palma Giovane. Fetti had no real followers in Venice, although it is instructive that the painter most influenced by him was the most Baroque of all, Francesco Maffei (?1605–60).

The German Johann Liss (c.1597–1629/30) paid a brief visit to Venice on his way to Rome in 1621 and returned late in the 1620s, dying there in the plague of 1629–30. In Venice he painted by about 1628 a single altarpiece, *The Vision of St Jerome* in S. Nicolò da Tolentino, and pictures by him are also recorded in Venetian collections (Savini-Branca 1965, *passim*). Liss's style by the time of his arrival in Venice was more truly Baroque than that of any other painter who had worked in the Veneto, and not surprisingly it was taken up by Maffei; but his true heirs in Venice were eighteenth-century painters such as Pittoni and Piazzetta.

Bernardo Strozzi (1581–1644) was already a colourist when he arrived in Venice in 1621. His exciting technique, with lavish impasto and an unusual mingling of hues in the painting of flesh [Nos.18–27], was taken up by a number of Venetian painters, and he had direct disciples in Ermanno Stroiffi (1616–93) [No.28] and Antonio Carneo (1637–92) [Fig.4]. In Venice Strozzi was at once patronised as a portraitist, a genre at which he excelled [Nos.18,20,27], and also quickly found favour as a painter of altarpieces [No.21], a number of which still survive in Venetian churches. He was also popular with collectors, a fact which almost certainly accounts for the number of versions of his compositions that survive, both by himself and by imitators [Nos.23,24].

The settling in Venice of Fetti, Strozzi and Liss set a pattern that was to be followed throughout the century of painters from outside the Veneto establishing themselves in the city. About 1625 the Fleming Nicolas Regnier, Italianised as Niccolò Renieri (1591–1667), who had worked in Rome in a manner at first close to the Caravaggisti, arrived and soon established himself as a fashionable painter. By then he had completely absorbed the lessons of Caravaggism into his own extremely sophisticated and elegant style, which during his Venetian period evolved little. Perhaps most important was Renieri's introduction into Venetian painting of Bolognese elements: in the work of a painter as late as Antonio Molinari (1665–c.1730) [No.49] one can find distant echoes of the languid females inspired by Guido Reni that one associates particularly with Renieri's art [No.29].

Figure 4
Antonio Carneo:
Lucretia. National
Museum, Warsaw.
99 × 82.5 cm.

Another Flemish settler in Venice at this time was Renieri's future son-in-law, Daniel van den Dyck (1614–70) [*No.32*].

The influence of Rome was brought to Venice through the work of Francesco Ruschi (*c.*1610–61) who between 1643 and 1656 painted a number of altarpieces, including the *Madonna in Glory with Saints* in S. Pietro di Castello [*Fig.5*]. In Rome Ruschi had been impressed by the highly decorative work of Pietro da Cortona. Whereas most seventeenth-century Venetian painters were inspired by Veronese in some aspect of their work, Ruschi's paintings in their overall effect can be truly described as neo-Veronesian. Making use of very grand compositions and rich architectural motifs, he set a trend which was to be followed by later seventeenth-century painters, among them Giovanni Antonio Fumiani (1650–1710) [*No.49*].

Figure 5
Francesco Ruschi:
*Madonna in Glory with
Saints*. S. Pietro di
Castello, Venice.
508 × 256 cm.

Other settlers in the mid-century included two painters from Tuscany, Pietro Ricchi (1606–75) and Sebastiano Mazzoni (c.1611–78). Ricchi was a native of Lucca who had been a pupil in Bologna of Guido Reni and later worked in France and Lombardy before settling in Venice for about twenty years from the late 1640s. His Venetian masterpiece is the *Adoration of the Magi* in S. Pietro di Castello, of about 1660. His style, which contains strong elements of the Milanese, is much less unusual than that of his compatriot, the Florentine Mazzoni, who early in his Venetian years painted two canvases with scenes from the life of St Benedict for the church of S. Benedetto (1648–49). Mazzoni is more associated with paintings of subjects drawn from literature, often obscure [*No.40*]; he was himself a poet, and there is evidence that he frequented Venetian literary circles.

The pupils of Padovanino

Following the example of their teacher, the pupils of Padovanino also returned to the painters of the Cinquecento, in particular to early Titian, and sought to reinterpret that style in a new idiom. Among the most important were Girolamo Forabosco (c.1604–72), Pietro della Vecchia (1603–78), Giulio Carpioni (1613–79) and Pietro Liberi (1614–87). Forabosco came from Padua, like his teacher, but he was in Venice probably by 1627. In his use of rich impasto he was influenced by the work of Strozzi. His masterpiece is the *Miraculous Salvation from Shipwreck* in the Duomo at Malamocco (Venice), but he is best known as a portraitist: in this genre his style is very distinctive, with highly decorative effects of flowers and costume, and a somewhat stark presentation of the sitter [*Fig.6*].

Pietro della Vecchia's reinterpretation of the art of the sixteenth century was idiosyncratic, and he was very prolific [*Nos.33,34*]. Among the best known of his paintings are those of soldiers in armour, fortune-tellers, gamblers and pairs of lovers, which were inspired by the sixteenth-century work of Giorgione, Romanino, Lotto and others, and indeed were occasionally believed to date from the Cinquecento. Of the Venetian painters he was perhaps the one most taken by the dramatic lighting effects of the Caravaggisti, employing them in his own paintings, though with results that can hardly ever be called Caravaggesque.

Padovanino's teaching also inspired Carpioni in a highly idiosyncratic way. He himself had copied the bacchanals of Titian, and through him Carpioni became interested in the bacchanal, which he developed into a form that was unique to him and among the most original inventions of the Italian Seicento [*No.38*]. His style was extremely linear [*No.39*]: it followed that he should excel as an etcher, and this aspect of his work influenced Tiepolo.

Pietro Liberi also looked at the early works of Titian, but translated them firmly into a Baroque language of his own, far advanced in manner beyond that of his teacher. Drawing on traditional subject-matter from mythology, the Bible [*No.37*] and literature, Liberi's best known works depict female nudes, generally distinctively Venetian in character, and include draperies and jewels painted so as

Figure 6
Girolamo
Forabosco:
*Portrait of a Venetian
Lady.*
Kunsthistorisches
Museum, Vienna.
78 × 64 cm.

to produce very ornamental effects. His pictures were extremely popular with collectors during his lifetime and also appealed to later artists, and he may perhaps be regarded as the most characteristically Venetian of the major painters working in the city in the seventeenth century.

The Baroque of Francesco Maffei

It is in the work of Francesco Maffei (?1605–60), an artist from Vicenza, where he lived most of his life, that the Baroque in Venetian painting finds its most individual and lively expression. Already before his move to Venice in 1638 he was well versed in the work of such painters as Jacopo Bassano and Veronese, from whom he derived his brilliant sense of colour as well as his compositions. In Venice he came under the influence of Strozzi and in particular of Liss and Fetti. Boschini in his *Carta del navegar pitoresco* praised him highly, calling him 'Caro Maffei . . . Pitor de tuta inteligenza', a painter 'not of dwarfs but of giants, his style amazing everyone, and his pictures which everyone looked at with open mouths'. Boschini laments Maffei's departure from Venice to settle in Padua and offers his condolences to unfortunate Vicenza at having lost so talented a son. Works by Maffei in Venetian churches are relatively few, and he does not seem to have been much sought after by Venetian collectors of the time: only six paintings by him are listed in the accounts of Venetian seventeenth-century collections by Savini-Branca (1965, *passim*); and his influence on later painters was not as great as the powerful nature of his style might suggest.

The tenebrist painters

Of all currents in Venetian seventeenth-century painting that which had the most profound repercussions is the work of a number of painters whose style is referred to as tenebrist. The early paintings of the Spanish artist Ribera, who worked in Naples from 1616, are characterised by a strong sense of realism expressed by his use of chiaroscuro, a very coarse rendering of the flesh, and a choice of somewhat brutal subject-matter. Allied to the general movement, under the influence of Caravaggio, towards a greater naturalism in Italian painting of the early Seicento, Ribera's style was highly influential and was taken up by a number of painters in Rome and other centres, not least in Venice. After settling in Naples Ribera never travelled, but his paintings were known elsewhere and his influence was extended through the early paintings of his pupil Luca Giordano, who worked in a similar vein. Giordano seems to have paid his first visit to Venice some time between 1652 and 1654, when he was still in his twenties, and probably at this time painted the altarpieces of the *Madonna delle Grazie* in S. Pietro di Castello and *The Deposition* for S. Maria del Pianto [*Fig.7*]. Ribera favoured studies of the nude, painting a number of pictures of aged male figures – philosophers, St Jerome, the Good Samaritan, etc. – and this type of subject was taken up by his pupil. The style of the young Giordano was new to the Veneto in the 1650s and it appealed to a number of painters there; but it was with the arrival some time late in the 1650s of Giovanni Battista Langetti (?1635–76), a Genoese painter who had worked in Rome and had taken up a Riberesque manner, that the influence of naturalism in Venetian Seicento painting was confirmed. From this moment a whole school of painters, the tenebrists, developed.

Langetti, whose style was much admired by the Venetians, was patronised in

Venice both privately and by the Church. Among his altarpieces is a *Christ on the Cross*, painted about 1664 for S. Teresa [*Fig.8*]. Boschini praised him greatly, saying that when painting his subject pictures of philosophers and saints he could work at great speed. Like Ribera and Giordano, Langetti had a taste for the gruesome and the macabre. In Venice, under the influence of a fellow Genoese, Strozzi, he developed a strong sense of colour which in some pictures, together with his very rich use of paint in areas of flesh, is extremely striking [*No.41*].

Langetti's style was immediately taken up by a contemporary, the German Johann Carl Loth (1632–98) [*Nos.42,43*], who came to Venice perhaps slightly earlier, around 1656, when he was a pupil of Pietro Liberi. Other painters in Venice soon adopted a tenebrist style, the most important among them being Antonio Zanchi (1631–1722), who in his early years worked very closely with

Figure 7 *(above left)* Luca Giordano: *The Deposition,* *c.*1652–54, from S. Maria del Pianto, Venice. Accademia, Venice. 447 × 243 cm.

Figure 8 *(above)* Giovanni Battista Langetti: *Christ on the Cross,* from S. Teresa, Venice. Ca' Rezzonico, Venice. 336 × 167 cm.

Loth. Tenebrism also affected the work of Pietro Negri (1628–79), for whom the elegance of Renieri was important as well [*Fig.9*]; Andrea Celesti (1637–1712), who worked alongside Zanchi in painting the huge lunettes in S. Zaccharia; and Strozzi's disciple Antonio Carneo (1637–92) [*Fig.4*].

Unlike Langetti, who remained a strict tenebrist until his death at the age of forty-one in 1676, Loth and Zanchi in their later work developed more colourful effects painted with an altogether lighter palette. This development paralleled that of Luca Giordano, and was guided by the paintings which he executed during later visits to Venice, particularly the altarpieces in the Salute, *The Assumption* of 1667 and *The Birth of the Virgin* and *The Presentation in the Temple* [*Fig.10*], slightly later in date but before 1674, when they were described by Boschini (Ferrari and Scavizzi 1966, II, pp.73,80). Also highly influential was Pietro da Cortona's altarpiece, *Daniel in the Lions' Den* [*Fig.11*], sent from Rome and installed in S. Daniele in 1663. The effect on Loth of these paintings is readily seen in his *St Joseph with the Christ Child* [*Fig.12*] in S. Silvestro, of 1681, which contains distinct echoes of the Roman High Baroque of such painters as Gaulli and Carlo Maratta, and in that prefigures Sebastiano Ricci. The later style of Zanchi was taken up by his follower Molinari.

Distinct from the work of the tenebrists was the realism of Pietro Bellotti (1625–1700), whose unusual paintings [*No.48*] were enormously popular. He was praised by Boschini with an enthusiasm equal to that lavished on Maffei.

Figure 10
Luca Giordano:
*The Presentation in
the Temple* c.1670–74.
S. Maria della
Salute, Venice.

Figure 11
Pietro da Cortona:
Daniel in the Lions' Den, 1663, from S. Daniele, Venice.
Accademia, Venice.
443 × 225 cm.

Figure 12
Johann Carl Loth:
St Joseph with the Christ Child, 1681. S. Silvestro, Venice.
385 × 188 cm.

Decorative painting and portraiture

Painted decoration was very much part of the Venetian tradition. Unfortunately Luca Giordano, who painted such work elsewhere, received no such commissions in Venice. Among the most important decorative schemes in the city of the last half of the seventeenth century is that in the Library of S. Giorgio, by two painters from Lucca who worked in Rome, Filippo Gherardi (1643–1717) and Giovanni Coli (1636–81) [*Fig.13*]. The ceiling dates from 1663–65 and the lunettes over the doors from 1665–68. Coli and Gherardi, echoing in their work the Roman High Baroque, with a strong decorative sense and use of bright colour, painted in a style that was opposed to the tenebrism prevalent in Venice in the 1660s; but they were in turn influenced by Venetian painting, and the S. Giorgio decorations are

Figure 13
Giovanni Coli and
Filippo Gherardi:
decoration in the
Library of S.
Giorgio Maggiore,
Venice, 1663–65.

very much in a neo-Veronesian style. In this they followed the example of Ruschi.

The work of Coli and Gherardi certainly affected the most ambitious Venetian decorative painter of the century, Giovanni Antonio Fumiani (1650–1710) [*No.49*], whose great ceiling for S. Pantalon, painted on canvas between 1684 and 1704, is one of the most elaborate masterpieces of Venetian, if not all Italian Baroque, painting. The ceiling is a virtuoso performance with architectural illusionism perfected to a very high degree, and it carries distinct echoes of the Venetian Cinquecento.

In the early years of the century Venetians looked for their portraits to, among others, Palma Giovane, Leandro Bassano (1557–1622), Sante Perando (1566–1638) and Marcantonio Bassetti, all of whom worked within the late

Figure 14
Tiberio Tinelli:
*Count Ludovico
Vidmano.* National
Gallery,
Washington.
206 × 137.5 cm.

sixteenth-century tradition. With the arrival of Strozzi in Venice in 1631 portraiture gained a new impetus: Strozzi became extremely popular [*Nos.18,20,27*] and his style was taken up by a number of painters. Among these Forabosco has already been mentioned. The most talented Venetian portraitist of the early part of the century, Tiberio Tinelli (1580–1638), who had trained under Leandro Bassano, was also influenced in his last decade by Strozzi [*Fig.14*]. Renieri and Daniel van den Dyck also painted portraits [*No.32*], as did Padovanino's pupils Carpioni, Pietro Liberi and Pietro della Vecchia. The influence of Strozzi lingered and is evident in the work of the two most talented portrait artists of the later part of this century, Sebastiano Bombelli (1635–1710) [*Fig.15*] and Niccolò Cassana (1659–1714) [*Fig.16*].

Figure 15
Sebastiano
Bombelli:
*Portrait of a
Procurator.*
Fondazione Querini
Stampalia, Venice.
232 × 159 cm.

Figure 16
Niccolò Cassana:
Portrait of a Child, said to be Thomas Thynne, 2nd Viscount Weymouth, signed N.(?) Cassana.
The Marquess of Bath, Longleat.
104.1 × 82.5 cm.

Figure 17 Gregorio Lazzarini: *The Charity of S. Lorenzo Giustiniani*. S. Pietro di Castello, Venice.

Figure 18 Paolo Pagani: *The Penitent Magdalen*. Staatliche Kunstsammlungen, Dresden. 115 × 149 cm.

The arrival of the eighteenth century

By the late seventeenth century the lightness and delicacy which one associates with Venetian paintings of the eighteenth century become apparent in the work of a number of painters: in such artists as Antonio Bellucci (1654–1726), Gregorio Lazzarini (1655–1730), Paolo Pagani (1660–1716) and Antonio Molinari (1665–c.1730) one may trace the transformation from the late tenebrism of Zanchi and Celesti to the highly decorative eighteenth-century style.

Bellucci, Lazzarini and Molinari all worked together in 1692 on frescoes (now destroyed) in the Sala Grande of the Palazzo Moro Lin on the Grand Canal, which had been built to the designs of Mazzoni for Pietro Liberi (who died in 1686). In Bellucci the two most important trends in Venetian Seicento painting are united – the decorative and colourful Baroque of Pietro Liberi and the chiaroscuro of the tenebrists [No.51]. Lazzarini had trained under Pietro della Vecchia and was much influenced by Forabosco and to a lesser extent by Carpioni, all three pupils of Padovanino. As he himself was the teacher of Giovanni Battista Tiepolo (1696–1770) he is fundamental to the evolution of Venetian painting from the work of Padovanino early in the seventeenth century to Tiepolo in the eighteenth. His paintings [Fig.17] are characterised by a strong sense of line (inspired by Carpioni), an academic approach to form and a certain sweetness in the types portrayed that is proto-eighteenth-century. He also painted portraits (for instance *Antonio Correr,* National Gallery No.3933). For Molinari the most important influence was Zanchi, but his palette is much lighter in tone [No.50]. To his pupil Piazzetta he brought a strong feeling for the work of the tenebrist painters. Pagani [Fig.18], who is less well known, worked in a style that resembles Molinari's, and had a feeling for bright clear colour which he passed to his pupil G. A. Pellegrini (1675–1741) [No.54]. In the work of Pellegrini and Sebastiano Ricci [No.53] eighteenth-century painting in Venice is born.

Venetian seventeenth-century painting and British collectors

Of all Venetian Seicento painters Domenico Fetti was by far the most sought after by early collectors of paintings in England. The Gonzaga collection which Charles I purchased from Mantua in 1629 included a number of paintings by the artist, who had recently worked at the Mantuan court (Millar 1958 and Levey 1964): a *Parable of the Good Samaritan, Eve Spinning* (now in the Louvre), *The Vision of St Peter* (now in Vienna), *David with the Head of Goliath* (Kensington Palace), *The Sacrifice of Elijah* [No.9] and a group of saints, called in early inventories 'ould friars', the majority of which are now at Hampton Court, including *St Barbara* [No.7]. In an inventory of the collection of the Duke of Buckingham made in 1635 (Davies 1907) there are no fewer than sixteen pictures which the Duke believed to be by Fetti, and the artist Lely also owned a *Tobit* by Fetti (Borenius 1943).

Another painter who enjoyed an early popularity in England was the German Johann Rottenhammer (1564–1625), from Munich, who had worked in Venice between 1596 and 1606: paintings by him were in the seventeenth-century collections of Charles I, the Earl of Arundel (Hervey 1921, pp.473 ff.) and the Duke of Buckingham.

Palma Giovane, whose style approximated well enough to the great Venetian painters of the sixteenth century (always much sought after in Britain), was also collected by contemporaries, including Charles I and Sir Peter Lely. The English Ambassador at Venice in the early years of the seventeenth century, Sir Henry Wotton, brought back with him a number of portraits of Doges by Odoardo Fialetti – bequeathed to Charles I and still in the Royal Collection [*Fig.2*] – and also bought in Venice an unfinished painting by Pietro Malombra, an artist who represented one of Boschini's *sette maniere*. Carlo Saraceni, Venetian by birth, was also known. Lely owned what was probably a version of his *Death of the Virgin* in S. Maria della Scala and also the *Spinario* (formerly Benedict Nicolson collection) which he believed to be by Saraceni, an attribution that is no longer accepted. Lord Fielding, Ambassador at Venice from 1634 to 1639, bought for his brother-in-law the Marquess of Hamilton a vast number of pictures, mainly by sixteenth-century painters, some of which were dispersed after the Civil War and are now in Vienna (Waterhouse 1952): they included pictures by Palma Giovane, Padovanino, Saraceni and Fetti. Fielding himself owned a version of Liss's *Gallant Couple* (Pommersfelden), which was sold at Christie's in 1938 as a *Portrait of Fielding and his Wife*. Fielding also noted for sale in Venice a picture, which he may have bought, of *Venus weeping with Adonis* by Renieri; and as Renieri is not known to have painted that subject it may in fact have been *Hero and Leander,* and possibly the painting by Renieri that was formerly in the collection of Lord Lonsdale at Lowther Castle and is now in Melbourne.

The most important British collection of Venetian seventeenth-century pictures was that formed by the 5th Earl of Exeter, who travelled in Italy in the 1680s and on subsequent occasions (Waterhouse 1960). He bought from Pietro Liberi no fewer than six paintings, which are still at Burghley [*Fig.19*], and also pictures by Celesti, Pietro della Vecchia [*No.34*] and Loth. *Jephtha's Vow,* now in the chapel at Burghley, was also possibly acquired at this time; at Burghley it is identified as Luca Giordano, but an attribution to Zanchi is more reasonable. The 2nd Earl of Sunderland also formed a collection of pictures in Italy in the seventeenth century, and they originally hung at Althorp (Garlick 1974–76). Fetti's *Mote and the Beam,* still there, was one of the Sunderland pictures; and the 1746 inventory records paintings by Strozzi and Fetti, including Fetti's *Hagar and the Angel* (still to be seen in the house), which may have been purchased by Lord Sunderland. Also at Althorp is a *Daedalus and Icarus* which was attributed in 1746 to Tintoretto and is now called Liberi, but which may in fact be by Maffei. A rare portrait of an Englishman by a Venetian seventeenth-century painter was that of the playwright Thomas Killigrew, who sat to Pietro Liberi for a portrait formerly at Thornham Hall, Norfolk, and now lost; and a *Portrait of a Child* by Niccolò Cassana at Longleat [*Fig.16*] is said to represent Thomas Thynne, 2nd Viscount Weymouth.

In the eighteenth century and later Venetian Seicento pictures continued to be

Figure 19
Pietro Liberi:
Pygmalion and Venus.
The Marquess of
Exeter, Burghley
House.
179 × 137.2 cm.

collected, although never to the extent of the Bolognese and Roman seventeenth-century schools. Attributions were more often than not extremely confused, and even an artist such as Fetti seems to have lost his popularity. It was for example possible for Consul Smith to sell George III Fetti's *Vincenzo Avogadro* [*No.8*] as a Van Dyck, and the same artist's *Elijah* [*No.9*], long in the Royal Collection and there known as a Fetti, was attributed to Aert de Gelder in the nineteenth century. Also in the nineteenth century, the 5th Duke of Northumberland was quite happy to purchase his Fetti of *The Blind Leading the Blind* [*No.13*] as a Schedone.

Later, the most popular Venetian seventeenth-century painter was Pietro della Vecchia [*Nos.33,34*]. The reason was almost certainly the same as that which had made him popular with his contemporaries: his pictures seemed such skilful pastiches of Venetian sixteenth-century paintings that they were perfectly acceptable to collectors whose real love was the Cinquecento. Pietro della Vecchia was represented in England in the late eighteenth- and early nineteenth-century collections of the Duke of Sutherland, Lord Lansdowne, Lord Dacres and others (Fröhlich-Bume 1952). Waagen in the 1850s listed pictures by him owned by Lord Northwick, Lord Lonsdale, the Duke of Hamilton, Lord Hardwick, Lord Malmesbury, Lord Yarborough and Smith Barry.

Palma Giovane, Padovanino and Damiano Mazza were all represented in British collections from an early stage and probably for the same reason as Pietro della Vecchia: their pictures looked sixteenth-century, and indeed were often believed to be by earlier painters. Thus Palma Giovane's *Mars and Venus* [*No.1*] was called Tintoretto, Mazza's *Ganymede* [*No.3*] was thought to be a Titian, an attribution also given to Mazza's *Allegory,* formerly in the collection of the Earl of Wemyss and now in Chicago (Tietze-Conrat 1945). Waagen listed pictures by Padovanino in the collections of the Marquess of Bute, the Duke of Sutherland and W. Stirling, and attributed to him a group of mythological paintings at Blenheim that were called Titian. The 4th Marquess of Bath bought some pictures in Venice late in the nineteenth century including Pietro Liberi's frieze illustrating the story of Circe still in the State Drawing Room at Longleat.

Bernardo Strozzi, remarkably, seems never to have been a particular favourite of the English, although by the 1750s both Lord Methuen and Lord Scarsdale owned pictures by him which are still respectively at Corsham and Kedleston [*No.22*]. In Lady Sunderland's sale in 1750 Strozzi's *Judith* [No.24] was called Italian School, and later it was attributed to Ippolito Galantini. Waagen listed a Strozzi *St Lawrence* in the collection of the Duke of Marlborough and a *Christ in the Temple* in that of the Duke of Northumberland. The *Bishop Saint* now in Chicago was owned by the Earl of Wilton in 1857, when he lent it to the Manchester Art Treasures Exhibition as a Lanfranco. Other Strozzis in British collections included *The Calling of St Matthew* (now in Worcester, Massachusetts), which was at Gatcombe Park in the early nineteenth century, and *The Adoration of the Shepherds* (Ashmolean), which was owned by John Strange in the late eighteenth century. Even in the present century Strozzi's identity has remained highly confused: his *Portrait of Bishop Alvise Grimani* (now in Washington) was sold at Christie's in 1902 as Van Dyck, and the *Design for a Basin* [*No.19*] sold in 1922 as Schiavone.

In the case of the remaining Venetian seventeenth-century painters there was complete confusion. Renieri may have been represented in British collections during the seventeenth century, as we have seen, and certainly was by the eighteenth [*No.30*]; indeed, all the paintings by him in the present exhibition [*Nos.29–31*] have been in England for some time. The names that have been attached to his paintings in the past include Giordano, Domenichino, Franceschini, Gentileschi, and that Caravaggesque painter most beloved of British collectors, Manfredi. Loth was sometimes believed in England to be Guercino or even Liss; Liss has been called Albani; and Langetti's works were attributed to Luca Giordano or Ribera. Mazzoni, not surprisingly, confounded all English connoisseurship and was labelled Salvator Rosa [*No.40*], a name which at least had the attraction of being perennially popular with British collectors.

Plate 1 Domenico Fetti *The Blind leading the Blind* (No.12)

Plate 2 Johann Liss *Judith with the Head of Holofernes* (No.17)

Plate 3 Bernardo Strozzi *A Concert* (No.23)

Plate 4 Bernardo Strozzi *Personifications of Summer and Spring* (No.26)

Plate 5
Niccolò Renieri
*St Sebastian
attended by
St Irene*
(No.31)

Plate 6
Francesco
Maffei
*The Adoration
of the Shepherds*
(No.35)

Plate 7
Johann
Carl Loth
Abraham and the
Angels (No.42)

Plate 8 Andrea Celesti *Imaginary Portrait of Count Alberto* (No.46)

Lenders

Figures refer to catalogue entries

Her Majesty the Queen 7, 8, 9, 23, 38, 52

Holburne of Menstrie Museum, University of Bath 41

Barber Institute of Fine Arts, University of Birmingham 12

City Museums and Art Gallery, Birmingham 18, 30, 32

The Earl of Bradford 44

The National Gallery of Ireland, Dublin 4, 15, 26, 33, 46

The Provost, Fellows and Scholars of Trinity College,
Dublin 39

The Governors of the Dulwich College Art Gallery 51

The Marquess of Exeter 14, 34

Ferens Art Gallery, City of Kingston upon Hull 31, 36

The Castle Howard Collection 10

Leicestershire Museum and Art Gallery, Leicester 29

Denis Mahon, Esq. 16

Manchester City Art Gallery 5

The National Trust (Polesden Lacey) 27

Northampton Art Gallery 45, 49, 50

The Duke of Northumberland 13

The Visitors of the Ashmolean Museum, Oxford 19, 28, 35

The Governing Body, Christ Church Oxford 24

The Viscount Scarsdale 22

Tyne and Wear County Council Museums (Shipley Art
Gallery, Gateshead) 42

York City Art Gallery 11

and those owners who wish to remain anonymous

Artists' Biographies

Antonio Balestra

Verona 1666 – Verona 1740

Balestra was a pupil in Venice from about 1687 of Antonio Bellucci (q.v.), and about 1690 went to Rome where he worked in the studio of Carlo Maratta. He visited Naples in 1694 and returned to Verona via Bologna in 1695. From 1697 to 1700 he lived in Venice and then, after visits to Parma, Piacenza and Milan, he settled in Verona in the early 1700s.

Balestra's style is rooted in Venetian painting, and in this the influence of his early teacher Bellucci is important. His Roman experience, and particularly the work of Maratta, led to a more formal 'classical' approach allied with a cooler sense of colour, which he imposed on the heritage of Venice. In his later years in Verona he was an important teacher, and numbered among his pupils Cignaroli, Nogari and Pietro Rotari.

Catalogue No.52

Marcantonio Bassetti

Verona 1586 – Verona 1630

Bassetti was, like Turchi (q.v.), a pupil in Verona of Felice Brusasorzi, but soon went to Venice. By early 1616 he was in Rome, together with his compatriots from Verona, Ottino and Turchi, and with them painted frescoes in the Sala Regia of the Quirinal Palace. About 1620 he returned to Verona, where he remained until his death in the plague of 1629–30.

In Venice Bassetti was impressed by the work of Tintoretto and of Jacopo Bassano, and became a friend of, and was influenced by, Palma Giovane (q.v.), who at the time was also working in a manner inspired by Tintoretto. In Rome Bassetti naturally came under the influence of Caravaggio, although he did not become a Caravaggist painter as such. His later work in Verona, particularly his portraits, shows some affinity with Fetti (q.v.), who had worked in neighbouring Mantua in 1613–22.

Literature: A. Ottani Cavina, 'Marcantonio Bassetti', in *Cinquant' anni di pittura veronese 1580–1630*, exhibition cat. (Verona, 1974) – here abbreviated as Ottani Cavina 1974.

Catalogue No.6

Pietro Bellotti

Bolzano 1625 – Gargnano sul Garda 1700

Bellotti was a pupil in Venice of Girolamo Forabosco, and himself became a noted portraitist who was widely patronised both within Italy and abroad, by, among others, the future Pope Alexander VII, Cardinal Mazarin and the court of the Elector Maximilian of Bavaria.

He was famous for his pictures representing single half-length figures treated in an extremely realistic manner, almost to the point of caricature, an aspect of his work which was praised by Zannetti. In this Bellotti approached, especially in his later paintings, the work of the Northern Caravaggisti. His interest in Dutch and Flemish paintings was probably fostered by Eberhard Keil, who brought with him to Venice, where he worked between 1651 and 1654, a taste for *bambocciante* painting.

Catalogue No.48

Antonio Bellucci

Venice 1654 – Treviso 1726

Bellucci may have been a pupil of Zanchi, and his style was formed under the opposing influences of the evolved tenebrism of that painter and the more decorative mode of Pietro Liberi (q.v.). As was the case with so many other painters of the late Venetian Seicento, the work of Luca Giordano in Venice in the 1670s also impressed him. Bellucci travelled in Europe and thereby established a precedent, followed by, among others, Sebastiano and Marco Ricci (q.v.), Pellegrini (q.v.) and the Tiepolos, for the employment of Venetian decorative painters abroad. From 1692 he worked for the palatine court in Germany and was also employed in Vienna, Lichtenstein and Düsseldorf. In 1716 he came to England, where he painted decorations for the chapel of the 1st Duke of Chandos at Canons Park in Middlesex (re-installed after 1747 at Great Witley, Worcestershire). He returned to Italy permanently only in 1722.

It is in the work of Bellucci, perhaps more than in that of any other painter, that the various currents in the development of Venetian seventeenth-century painting come together for the first time. His style also marks the triumph of Veronese over all other masters – Titian, Tintoretto, the Bassani, Ribera and the Caravaggisti, even Luca Giordano – as the true ancestor of eighteenth-century painting in Venice.

Catalogue No.51

Giulio Carpioni

Venice 1613 – Vicenza 1679

Carpioni was a pupil in Venice of Padovanino. Although a stay in Rome is not documented, such a visit during his formative years seems almost certain. From 1638 until the end of his life he lived in Vicenza. In addition to painting, he was also an extremely gifted etcher.

It seems most likely that Carpioni's very distinctive type of painting – some portraits, but mainly pictures of subjects drawn from mythology – was influenced by the bacchanals of Titian, Pietro Testa and Poussin. If he spent some time in Rome he would have come under the influence of Caravaggism, and he was certainly affected by the Caravaggesque Venetian work of Saraceni (q.v.) and Le Clerc, and also that of Turchi (q.v.), Ottino and Bassetti (q.v.) in Verona. From these sources Carpioni developed his highly unusual and instantly recognisable style. Orlandi (1704) says that Carpioni 'employed his talent in working on a small scale, applying himself to ideal inventions like dreams, sacrifices, bacchanals, triumphs and dancing putti and the most beautiful capricci, which never would have been invented by another painter'. All of these genres Carpioni treated in a highly linear manner. His light tends to coldness and there is a strong, although by no means dramatic, contrast between areas of light and dark within a composition. In the type of composition for which he is most famous, Carpioni, who was introverted in temperament though also witty, created a world of his own – a world tinged with nostalgia and melancholy and sometimes approaching the unreal.

Literature: G. M. Pilo, *Carpioni* (Venice, 1961), with catalogue raisonné – here abbreviated as Pilo 1961/2.

Catalogue Nos.38,39

Andrea Celesti

Venice 1637 – Toscolana 1712

Celesti was first a pupil in the studio of Matteo Ponzone, where he knew Zanchi (q.v.), and later he worked with Sebastiano Mazzoni (q.v.), but his style developed more under the powerful influence in Venice of Maffei (q.v.). Although he never worked in the strictly naturalistic vein of the tenebrists, Langetti (q.v.), Loth (q.v.) and Zanchi, he was impressed by their style. Like so many of his contemporaries in Venice, he lightened his palette as a result of contact with the later paintings executed in Venice by Luca Giordano. From 1688 he worked frequently outside Venice, in Lombardy.

Celesti, whose figure types are quite distinctive, with pointed noses and staring eyes, painted a number of religious canvases for churches in Venice, the Veneto and Lombardy, and also easel pictures with subjects drawn from history and mythology. Portraits by him are rare. The Venetian painters whom he himself influenced include Gregorio Lazzarini, Bellucci (q.v.) and Giuseppe Nogari.

Literature: A. M. Mucchi and C. della Croce, *Il pittore Andrea Celesti* (Milan, 1954), with catalogue raisonné – here abbreviated as Mucchi and della Croce 1954.

Catalogue Nos.46,47

Domenico Fetti

Rome *c.*1588/89 – Venice 1623

Fetti was a pupil in Rome of the Florentine painter Cigoli and early worked there under the patronage of Ferdinando Gonzaga. When the latter became Duke of Mantua, Fetti followed him north and worked at the Mantuan court from 1613. In 1618 he travelled in Tuscany and in 1621 went to Venice to purchase paintings for the Duke, returning the same year. He was back in Venice by September 1622, and died there on 16 April in the following year.

From his earliest years Fetti was interested perhaps most of all in Venetian painting, and it was therefore fitting that he himself should die in Venice. The influence of Cigoli was relatively slight, and Fetti was impressed more by the landscape paintings of Elsheimer and the Venetian Saraceni (q.v.) than by the large-scale work of the Caravaggisti.

Fetti was already attracted by Rubens' use of colour before his move to Mantua, where Rubens had also worked, and there the affinity between the two was substantiated. The collection of pictures belonging to the Gonzagas, particularly those of the Venetian sixteenth century, brought Fetti into close contact with the work of those painters whom he most admired. At least two of his compositions, *The Flight from Sodom* and *The Blind leading the Blind* (here exhibited, No.12) are derived directly from Veronese, and his *Flight into Egypt* (Vienna) comes from Tintoretto's *Flight* in the Scuola di S. Rocco, Venice.

With the exception of portraits, at which he excelled, Fetti was at his best when working on a small scale, and what was probably a commission from the Gonzagas to execute a series of small paintings with subjects drawn from the parables and sayings of Christ resulted in his most individual and lasting contribution to Italian seventeenth-century painting. In his treatment of parables, Fetti perfected a genre which already had some tradition in the Veneto (see further under No.11). Most of his parable pictures, which were executed in the last years of his life, were repeated by Fetti in a number of versions. As in the case of Strozzi (q.v.) and Renieri (q.v.), this practice probably owed as much to the whims of contemporary Venetian collectors as to those of the artists themselves.

Fetti's life was short, and if any development in his art can be discerned it is a lightening of his palette as he grew older. His technique is distinctive, with a strong emphasis on the poses of figures and rapid brush strokes of colour applied across the surface of more broadly painted areas, creating important effects of light. Although his pictures were certainly copied, his painting of parables was not taken up by any later painters, and he had no followers as such. Of all Venetian seventeenth-century painters it was Maffei (q.v.) who derived most from him.

Catalogue Nos.7–15

Giovanni Antonio Fumiani

Venice 1650 – Venice 1710

Fumiani studied in Bologna under Domenico Ambrogi, a *quadrature* and perspective painter, and by 1668 was back in Venice where he remained until his death.

His masterpiece, and indeed of its type conceivably the greatest masterpiece of Venetian Seicento painting, is the entire ceiling decoration on canvas of the church of S. Pantalon in Venice, which he executed between 1684 and 1704.

In Bologna Fumiani was interested in the work of the Carracci, in particular Ludovico Carracci, and on his return to Venice he sought inspiration in the decorative work of Veronese. In this he opposed the contemporary fashion for the tenebrist painting of Langetti (q.v.) and his followers. In returning to the example of Veronese, Fumiani followed the steps already taken by the older Francesco Ruschi (d.1661). The decorations which the Lucchese painters Giovanni Coli and Filippo Gherardi painted between 1663 and 1665 in the Library of S. Giorgio Maggiore also influenced him.

Fumiani's training under a *quadrature* painter makes itself apparent in most of his work, for in the painting of architecture, which occupies an important compositional role in most of his pictures, he reveals a very real and rare gift, which it should be said is not best exemplified by the picture here exhibited.

Catalogue No.49

Giovanni Battista Langetti

Genoa ?1635 – Venice 1676

Langetti's date of birth is given by Ratti (1769) as 1625, but documents relating to his death in 1676 state that he was then forty-one (Stefani 1966, p.222). A further complication is that a baptismal record for a Giovanni Battista Langetti, who may be the painter, is dated 1621 (Sagep 1971, p.166). Langetti moved to Rome at an early date and there worked in the studio of Pietro da Cortona. Towards the end of the 1650s he settled in Venice where, with the exception of visits to Bergamo and Florence, he remained until his death in 1676. Initially in Venice he worked with another Genoese, G. F. Cassana.

In Rome Langetti came under the influence of Caravaggism, particularly Ribera's version of it, and it is possible that he also visited Naples, where Ribera worked. In following Ribera's naturalism, Langetti's painting echoes that of the young Luca Giordano. Stefani (1966, p.202) has drawn attention to the fact that Langetti had a quasi-scientific interest in anatomy. The work of Langetti and Giordano introduced a highly important new current into Venetian Seicento painting: although relatively young when he settled in Venice, Langetti became the leader of the Venetian tenebrist painters, who included the German Loth (q.v.), the young Zanchi (q.v.), Pietro Negri, Antonio Carneo and to an extent even Celesti (q.v.). It was this strain in Venetian seventeenth-century painting that found its ultimate flowering in the eighteenth-century work of such painters as Piazzetta.

Langetti's typical subject-matter involves aged male nude figures – Job, Cato, Archimedes, the Good Samaritan – painted dramatically and with a realistic rendering of the flesh, and his pictures consciously convey a strong feeling for humanity. They are painted in the spirit of the Counter-Reformation, to illustrate the teaching of the Bible (in which Langetti was well versed), particularly with regard to the multiple aspects of sin and salvation.

Catalogue No.41

Pietro Liberi

Padua 1614 – Venice 1687

Liberi is thought to have been first in Venice in 1628, and may then have been in the studio of Padovanino. In the same year he went to Constantinople. Between 1632 and 1638 he travelled on a Greek ship to Tunisia, Malta, Sicily, Portugal and Spain. From 1638 to 1641 he was in Rome, and after travels in Northern Italy he settled in Venice in 1643. In 1658–59 he visited Hungary, Germany and Vienna.

Liberi is of prime importance for the development of Venetian Baroque painting, in that he transformed the Titianesque style of his teacher Padovanino into a full Baroque idiom.

In Rome Liberi was influenced by the work of the Carracci, and especially by that of Pietro da Cortona. What was probably the second visit of Luca Giordano to Venice in 1667 also affected his style, resulting in a freer use of colour. Contact in Venice with the Florentine Sebastiano Mazzoni (q.v.), a close friend, was also fruitful, and from this variety of sources, allied with his wide experience of travel, Liberi evolved a style which, in its maturity, was fully of the seventeenth century. His beautiful painting of skies and stuffs – rich brocades and silks – owes much to the example of Veronese, and in turn influenced his younger contemporaries, including Gregorio Lazzarini (q.v.), Antonio Molinari (q.v.) and Bellucci (q.v.). Through them, Liberi was the artistic ancestor of such eighteenth-century Venetian painters as Pellegrini (q.v.), Sebastiano Ricci (q.v.) and even Guardi.

Catalogue No.37

Johann Liss (or Jan Lys)

Oldenburg *c.*1597 – Venice 1629/30

Both Liss's parents may have been painters. Between about 1615 and 1619 he seems to have been in Haarlem, Amsterdam and Antwerp. From there he went to Paris, and then arrived in Venice no later than 1621. By 1622 he was probably in Rome, where he worked until the mid- to late 1620s. By 1629 he was definitely settled in Venice. A victim of the Venetian plague of 1629–30, Liss was no more than thirty-three at the time of his death.

Liss's oeuvre consists of relatively few paintings, executed within a fairly short time span. They show him working in a variety of styles, and reflect a considerable diversity of influences. His very earliest paintings are Dutch-inspired and depict peasant scenes or gallant couples in interiors. With the move to Antwerp, and contact with the paintings of Rubens, Abraham Janssens and in particular Jordaens, his approach became more realistic. On his first stay in Venice it was Fetti (q.v.), who was dead by the time of his return, who affected Liss most, demonstrating that it was possible to translate into Italianate terms the genre-like paintings of Liss's early youth. In Rome, Liss was at first most powerfully influenced by Caravaggio and the Caravaggisti, but he also looked at painters as divergent as Elsheimer and the Northern landscapists, Paul Brill and Cornelius Poelemburg; the Carracci; and Domenichino and Albani. His second stay in Venice was probably much shorter than has until recently been believed, and accordingly few paintings can be dated to that period.

With Fetti (who died in 1623) and Strozzi (q.v.), who did not arrive in Venice until 1631) Liss had a great influence on later Venetian painters, in his case particularly those of the eighteenth century. Among the artists most affected by him were Maffei (q.v.), Langetti (q.v.) and Loth (q.v.), and, in the eighteenth century, Piazzetta, Pittoni, Sebastiano Ricci (q.v.) and, to some extent, the Tiepolos. His proto-Rococo *St Jerome* altarpiece in S. Nicolò da Tolentino, Venice, became one of the most copied of all Venetian pictures.

Literature: Johann Liss, exhibition cat. (Augburg Rathaus and Cleveland Museum of Art, 1975–76); K. Steinbart, *Johann Liss, der Maler aus Hollstein* (Berlin, 1940); K. Steinbart, *Johann Liss* (Vienna, 1946) – here abbreviated as *Liss* 1975–76, Steinbart 1940 and Steinbart 1946 respectively.

Catalogue Nos.16,17

Johann Carl Loth

Munich 1632 – Venice 1698

The son of a painter, Loth was in Rome for two or three years before settling by about 1656 in Venice, where he remained for the rest of his life. Traditionally he is said to have been a pupil in Venice of Pietro Liberi (q.v.), although as Lanzi (1789) justly pointed out, if that is the case Loth did not follow in the footsteps of his teacher. Instead, in his first years in Venice Loth was influenced by the Genoese Langetti (q.v.), and, like him, developed a tenebrist style derived from Ribera and the young Luca Giordano. His work of this period comes close to that of his contemporary Zanchi (q.v.), with whom on occasion he worked.

By the time of the death of Langetti in 1676 Loth's style was developing into a lighter and altogether more decoratively elegant vein. In this he was influenced by the work of Pietro da Cortona, whose important altarpiece *Daniel in the Lions' Den* (Accademia, Venice) was installed in the church of S. Daniele in Venice in 1663. At this mature stage of his career the influence of Pietro Liberi at last becomes apparent. Loth's later work may be said to echo to an extent the Roman High Baroque of painters such as Gaulli and even Carlo Maratta. This phase of Loth's work influenced Molinari (q.v.) and, through him, the latter's pupil Piazzetta and other painters of the early eighteenth century in Venice such as Sebastiano Ricci (q.v.) and Pellegrini (q.v.).

Literature: G. Ewald, *Johann Carl Loth, 1632–1698* (Amsterdam, 1965), with catalogue raisonné – here abbreviated as Ewald 1965.

Catalogue Nos. 42, 43

Francesco Maffei

Vicenza ?1605 – Padua 1660

Maffei went to Venice about 1638, but was back in Vicenza in the 1640s and 1650s and finally in 1657 settled in Padua, where he died three years later.

He was one of the more important painters of the Venetian Seicento. His style was formed under the influence of Jacopo Bassano, Tintoretto and Veronese, but his move to Venice and contact with the paintings of Strozzi (q.v.), Fetti (q.v.) and Liss (q.v.) greatly increased the Baroque tendencies in his work, particularly with regard to colour.

The paintings dating from his maturity are highly individual. Exaggerated and wild, his compositions unite the realms of heaven and earth in a vision of pyrotechnics. His figures, ranging from the exotic to the grotesque and painted in the most dramatic and brilliant colours, fuse with the settings – sky, landscape and architecture – in which they are placed. After his move to Padua his work is much calmer. (The *Annunciation* exhibited here, No.36, dates from that period.) Maffei was a true heir to the tradition of Veronese, which he translated firmly into the Baroque, and his work in turn influenced the painters of the Venetian eighteenth century, Sebastiano Ricci (q.v.) and Tiepolo among them.

Literature: N. Ivanoff, *Catalogo della Mostra di F. Maffei* (Venice, 1956) – here abbreviated as Ivanoff 1956.

Catalogue Nos. 35, 36

Damiano Mazza

active 1573

Mazza was born in Padua. No dates for him are known except for that of one documented work, *The Ascension of Christ* at Noale in the Veneto, of 1573. He was a pupil and imitator of Titian and, according to Ridolfi (1648), died while still young, though he may have died as late as 1628 (Fiocco 1929/2, p.11).

Mazza's importance for the Venetian Seicento lies in the fact that he continued the manner of Titian into the final years of the sixteenth century, and influenced Padovanino (q.v.), a fellow Paduan, who was the most important teacher in early seventeenth-century Venice.

Catalogue No. 3

Sebastiano Mazzoni

Florence *c.*1611 – Venice 1678

Mazzoni is known as a painter, a poet and an architect. He may have visited Venice some time in the 1630s and returned in the next decade, possibly encouraged by Pietro Liberi (q.v.), to settle there, remaining until his death.

He is said to have been a pupil of Cristofano Allori, although, as that painter died in 1621, this seems unlikely. Mazzoni's unusual style, which was formed in the Florentine *ambiente* of Francesco Furini and the latter's pupil Pignone, is sometimes confused with that of another Florentine, Cecco Bravo. In Venice Mazzoni was influenced, particularly with regard to technique, by the works of Strozzi (q.v.); and his sense of composition developed with direct knowledge of Veronese and Tintoretto. He was extraordinarily inventive in both choice and treatment of subject-matter, and his paintings are characterised by a wild, windswept busyness – at times fantastic or disturbing – and elaborate and sophisticated treatment of perspective.

Mazzoni's style was very rare. He trained Niccolò Bambini and, according to some sources that are probably mistaken, Sebastiano Ricci (q.v.) as well, and his work influenced a number of Venetian Seicento painters, including in particular Fumiani (q.v.) and Celesti (q.v.).

Catalogue No.40

Antonio Molinari

Venice 1665 – Venice c.1730

The son of the painter Giovanni Molinari, by whom he was presumably taught, Antonio Molinari remained in Venice all his life and died there some time after 1728 and before 1734.

In the 1690s Molinari painted some scenes from the life of St Catherine for the church of the same name in Vicenza: other paintings in the series were executed by his father, by Celesti (q.v.), by Fumiani (q.v.) and by Zanchi (q.v.), and of these it was the paintings of Zanchi that most affected him. From Zanchi, whose style by this time had evolved from an early naturalism into a more decorative phase, Molinari derived the composition and figure types which he employed particularly in his easel paintings. With some additional influence from Pietro Negri, Molinari created paintings which were to determine the art of the early eighteenth century in Venice, particularly the work of such painters as Bellucci (q.v.) and Pellegrini (q.v.).

For the transmission of his style, Molinari's contact as early as 1692 with Gregorio Lazzarini and Bellucci, when all three worked on the frescoes in the Sala Grande of the Palazzo Moro-Lin on the Grand Canal in Venice (designed by Mazzoni, q.v.) was important. Molinari also had as a pupil Piazzetta, whose style derives so much from the Venetian tenebrist painters of the seventeenth century; and Piazzetta's development, together with that of Pellegrini and Bellucci, underlines Molinari's importance as a link between the seventeenth and eighteenth centuries.

Catalogue No.50

Alessandro Varotari, called Il Padovanino

Padua 1588 – Venice 1648

Padovanino was himself the son of a painter, though in his youth he was more influenced by the Titianesque manner of Damiano Mazza (q.v.). He settled in Venice in 1614, and early paid a visit to Rome where he copied the bacchanals of Titian (including *Bacchus and Ariadne,* National Gallery No.35) then in the collection of Cardinal Aldobrandini but originally at Ferrara. After his return to Venice by 1618 he remained there until his death in 1648.

Padovanino's style was modelled on that of the young Titian, from whom he derived although by no means copied his compositions, figures, and colour, and he sought to continue the Titianesque tradition into the Seicento. In Rome he was interested in the work of the Bolognese, in particular Albani and Domenichino, and also in Raphael.

Padovanino's allegiance to Titian meant not only that his work could seem old-fashioned, but also that it was opposed to the prevailing style of his Venetian contemporaries, particularly Palma (q.v.). Nevertheless, it was Padovanino who brought to a whole new generation of painters in Venice a feeling for the great age of Venetian painting in the sixteenth century, and his importance as a teacher can scarcely be overestimated. Through his teaching a whole group of seventeenth-century painters – Girolamo Forabosco, Pietro Liberi (q.v.), Carpioni (q.v.) and Pietro della Vecchia (q.v.) among them – returned to the example of the Venetian Cinquecento and derived from it their own distinctive styles, which in turn determined the development of later Seicento painting.

Catalogue No.4

Iacopo or Giacomo Palma, called Palma Giovane

Venice c.1548 – Venice 1628

His real name was Giacomo Negretti Palma, but he was called Palma Giovane to distinguish him from his great-uncle, the painter Palma Vecchio. Ridolfi (1648) gives his birth date as 1544, but Stefania Mason Rinaldi has drawn attention to a variety of factors which indicate that he was born about 1548. In 1564 he was called to the court at Urbino by Duke Guidobaldo. There he copied the work of Titian and Raphael and also probably became acquainted with Barocci. The same patron sent him to Rome where he spent perhaps about three years, returning to Venice in 1570.

In Venice he entered the studio of Titian, on the death of whom he finished that artist's painting of the *Pietà* now in the Accademia, Venice. Palma came on the Venetian scene at an important time. Titian died in 1576, Veronese in 1588 and Tintoretto in 1594, and it was to Palma, who was enormously prolific, that most of the important church and civic commissions fell. According to Ridolfi (1648) he was patronised by the architect Vittoria, who was at the time dissatisfied with Tintoretto and Veronese. Although he was trained by Titian, and influenced to an extent by that painter's early work, it was the compositions and lighting effects of Tintoretto that exerted most influence on Palma, and he in turn dominated the whole generation of painters born between the years 1550 and 1570.

Catalogue No.1

Giovanni Antonio Pellegrini

Venice 1675 – Venice 1741

Pellegrini was a pupil of Paolo Pagani in Venice. He went to England in 1708 and remained until 1713, then went to Düsseldorf and the Low Countries, and returned to England for some months in 1719–20. He was subsequently based in Venice from where he travelled widely in Europe.

Unlike the work of Sebastiano Ricci (q.v.), whose style was formed under a variety of influences and not only in Venice, Pellegrini's painting is entirely Venetian in spirit, and represents more clearly than Ricci's a logical culmination of seventeenth-century Venetian painting. At its simplest, this development runs from the tenebrism of Zanchi (q.v.) through the lighter and more decorative Molinari (q.v.) to the brilliantly sunny Pellegrini. Pellegrini's teacher, Pagani, was probably the pupil of Pietro Liberi (q.v.), and this link serves to anchor Pellegrini even more firmly within the Venetian tradition. From Molinari Pellegrini derived his figure types, some compositions, and his choice of subject-matter which invariably centres on themes traditional in Venetian painting.

Catalogue No.54

Niccolò Renieri (Nicolas Regnier)

Maubeuge 1591 – Venice 1667

Renieri was a pupil at Antwerp of Abraham Janssens, and in about 1615 went to Rome.

Sandrart (1683) says he was patronised by Caravaggio's patron Vincenzo Giustiniani, who took him into his household (see further under No.30 here exhibited). He was still in Rome in 1624 and probably settled in Venice about 1624/25 after a possible visit to Bologna where his step-brother, Desulbeo, lived. In Venice he was extremely popular and fashionable, and himself formed a collection of pictures. Two of his four daughters, Lucrezia and Clorinda, married painters, Daniel van den Dyck (q.v.) and Pietro della Vecchia (q.v.); and his daughters were also painters.

From Venice on occasion Renieri went to work at the courts of Modena and Mantua. In Rome he came under the influence of the Caravaggisti, in particular Manfredi and the French artists Vouet and Tournier, but he used Caravaggism – in particular the effects of light and sharp contrasts – to enhance a sense of luxury in his pictures, with beautiful silks, jewellery and metals elegantly painted. Later, under the influence of Guido Reni, he developed the type of languishing and abandoned female who masquerades as the Magdalen, Sophonisba, Artemisia, Cleopatra and others in the pictures with which his name is most associated. After his initial years in Venice, his work, though talented, became stereotyped, and there was little development in his style, which can make the dating of his pictures difficult. Among the Venetian painters most influenced by him were the young Carpioni (q.v.), Pietro Negri, Ruschi and Molinari (q.v.).

Literature: P. L. Fantelli, 'Nicolò Renieri, pittor fiamengo', in *Saggi e Memorie di Storia dell'Arte*, IX, 1974, pp.77 ff., with catalogue raisonné – here abbreviated as Fantelli 1974/1.

Catalogue Nos.29–31

Sebastiano Ricci

Belluno 1659 – Venice 1734

According to Pascoli (1736) Ricci went at the age of twelve to Venice, where he was apprenticed to Federico Cervelli, and at the age of twenty-nine moved to Bologna and worked with Giovanni Gioseffo dal Sole. Temanza (1738) says that Mazzoni (q.v.) was his first teacher. From the second half of the 1680s Ricci was patronised by Duke Ranuccio Farnese, and travelled widely in Northern Italy and to Rome. Probably in 1702 he first travelled abroad, to Germany, Austria, France, Flanders and England, where he stayed from 1711/12 to 1716. He finally settled in Venice in 1717, and died there seventeen years later.

It was Ricci, with his brilliantly joyous use of colour, who much more than his contemporary Bellucci (q.v.) transformed the heritage of Veronese into an entirely Rococo idiom. Although he certainly referred to the work of the Venetian painters of the seventeenth century, in particular Francesco Maffei (see, for example, No.36 here exhibited), his style is Veronesian. Contact with the highly individual painter Alessandro Magnasco led, especially in his later work, to a more feathery use of paint which prefigures Guardi. In Rome he came under the influence in particular of Gaulli. He can be regarded as the father of Venetian eighteenth-century painting: and from him painters of much greater talent, such as the Tiepolos, developed, and painted pictures which are among the masterpieces of Western art.

Literature: J. Daniels, *Sebastiano Ricci* (Hove, 1976) and by the same author *L' opera completa di Sebastiano Ricci* (Milan, 1976) – here abbreviated as Daniels 1976/1 and Daniels 1976/2.

Catalogue No.53

Carlo Saraceni
Venice 1579 – Venice 1620

Saraceni may have been a pupil of Palma Giovane in Venice but went to Rome in 1598 and there became interested in Caravaggism, particularly Gentileschi's interpretation of it. He was also inspired by the small-scale work of the Northern landscapists working in Rome, notably Elsheimer. By 1613 he had moved to Mantua, where he was employed at the ducal court, and he remained there until about 1619 when he returned to Venice, where he died in the following year.

In his treatment of landscape Saraceni was inspired by the sixteenth-century landscape painters of the Veneto – Lotto, Romanino, Savoldo and Giorgione – but, under the influence of Elsheimer and his circle, he created landscapes which are distinctly his own. His paintings, on a large scale and generally religious in subject-matter, are Caravaggesque in idiom but have a soft and tender gentleness.

Saraceni's return to Venice for the last year of his life and the paintings which he executed for the city were highly important for the subsequent development of Venetian Seicento painting. By bringing Caravaggism at first hand to the Veneto, Saraceni introduced an entirely new strain. His use of light, and his direct and even realistic style, were overtly opposed to the manner of Padovanino

(q.v.), then the principal teacher in Venice, but some artists such as Pietro della Vecchia (q.v.) and Giulio Carpioni (q.v.) were able to draw from both painters in their development of their own highly individual styles.

Literature: A. Ottani Cavina, *Carlo Saraceni* (Milan, 1968), with catalogue raisonné – here abbreviated as Ottani Cavina 1968.

Catalogue No.2

Ermanno Stroiffi
Padua 1616 – Venice 1693

Zanetti (1771) says that Stroiffi was a disciple of Strozzi (q.v.), whose style at first he imitated, and Boschini remarks how their works were sometimes confused. Few paintings by him are known, but a *Pietà* certainly by him in S. Tomaso Cantauriense in Padua of about 1650 demonstrates, particularly in the facial type, how close his style came to that of Strozzi.

Stroiffi became a priest in 1647 and founded the congregation of Philippines in Padua.

Catalogue No.28

Bernardo Strozzi, sometimes called Il Prete Genovese or Il Cappuccino
Genoa 1581 – Venice 1644

Strozzi is said by Soprani (1674) to have been a pupil in Genoa of Pietro Sorri and later of Cesare Corte. About 1597 he became a Capuchin friar (hence his nicknames), and at this time he painted pictures with single figures of saints, in particular St Francis, which are today known in several examples. About 1610 he was permitted to leave the monastery to care for his sick and widowed mother, and continued painting in and around Genoa. On the death of his mother in 1630, Strozzi seems to have sought to leave the Capuchins and join the Lateran Canons Regular. He is last recorded in Genoa in September 1630 and probably by 1631 he was in Venice, where he settled.

Strozzi, who was destined to be one of the more influential painters of the Italian Seicento, derived his style from the variety of manners available to him in the Genoa of his youth. The city had substantial commercial links with Flanders, and a significant number of Flemish painters were working there in the late sixteenth and early seventeenth centuries. The most important of them for Strozzi, indeed for any artist, was Rubens, whose

Circumcision altarpiece (painted in Rome) was installed in S. Ambrogio in 1605, and who was himself in Genoa in 1607. Although Strozzi's style was formed by the time of Van Dyck's first visit to Genoa in 1621, there probably was some cross-fertilization between the two. The tradition of still-life painting which finds expression in Flemish art (numerous examples of which existed in Genoa) was also important to Strozzi, who from an early age included some still-life in many of his paintings. Another influence was the distinctive colour of Federico Barocci, whose huge *Crucifixion* was installed in Genoa Cathedral in 1597. Caravaggism reached the young Strozzi via Orazio Gentileschi, who was in Genoa in 1621, and also through the latter's Genoese follower Domenico Fiasella. There was strong Milanese influence on the painters of Genoa in the early years of the seventeenth century; and from such artists as Cerano, and in particular G. C. Procaccini, who worked in Genoa from 1618, Strozzi derived not only the compositional types of his early single-figure saints but also the flashes of brilliantly deep greens and reds which one finds in paintings by him throughout his career.

Strozzi's style was established by the time he reached Venice in 1631, and it is not always easy to distinguish with certainty between his late Genoese and early Venetian work. In Venice it was the painting of Veronese which interested him most. With Fetti (q.v.) and Liss (q.v.) he was one of a trio of 'foreign' painters working in the city in the first half of the century who had enormous influence on the subsequent development of Venetian painting. Though much lighter in tone, Strozzi's painting prefigured the tenebrists of the mid-century, Langetti (q.v.), Loth (q.v.) and Zanchi (q.v.). The painters most affected by his style were Stroiffi (q.v.) and Carneo, and to an extent Forabosco; but others as well – the young Pietro della Vecchia (q.v.), Maffei (q.v.) and, on his arrival in Venice, Mazzoni (q.v.) – absorbed Strozzi's technique and colour and made them part of the Venetian tradition.

Literature: L. Mortari, *Bernardo Strozzi* (Rome, 1966), with catalogue raisonné – here abbreviated as Mortari 1966.

Catalogue Nos. 18–27

Alessandro Turchi, also called L'Orbetto

Verona 1578 – Rome 1649

Turchi's date of birth is now known to be 1578, although Zannandreis (1891) gives 1581 and Mancini (1617) 1588/90. He was first a pupil at Verona of Felice Brusasorzi. The early accounts of his life (Dal Pozzo 1718, Passeri 1675–79 and Lanzi 1789) give conflicting accounts of a sojourn in Venice during his youth, but it is now by no means certain that Turchi ever worked in Venice. Probably about 1614/15 he went to Rome (he was certainly there by 1616), where he came into contact with the Venetian Saraceni (q.v.), and he remained there for the rest of his life.

With Marcantonio Bassetti (q.v.) and Pasquale Ottino, Turchi formed a trio of Veronese painters working in Rome in the early decades of the seventeenth century. Their style, in particular that of Turchi and Ottino, was based on a study of Raphael, Correggio and the Carracci. Of the three, Turchi was most influenced by Caravaggism, which he transposed into a soft and tender, almost sentimental, key, particularly in the painting of nudes. Many of his smaller pictures are on slate.

Turchi is also known as 'L'Orbetto' (the little blind boy) because his father, whom as a child he always accompanied, was blind.

Literature: D. Scaglietti, in *Cinquant'anni di pittura veronese 1580–1630,* exhibition cat. (Verona, 1974) – here abbreviated as Scaglietti 1974.

Catalogue No. 5

Daniel van den Dyck

Antwerp 1614 – Mantua 1670

Van den Dyck was in Italy by 1633, when he worked at Bergamo: some portraits from that time are now in the Accademia Carrara there. By 1634 he was in Venice, where he remained until 1657. He then moved to Mantua to work at the ducal court. He married a daughter of Niccolò Renieri (q.v.).

There is an altarpiece by Van den Dyck in the church of the Madonna dell'Orto in Venice painted in a somewhat Rubensesque style, but it is as a portraitist that he shows himself at his most characteristic. His use of paint owes something to Fetti (q.v.), and he was also influenced by Renieri, though his style is much less hard and indeed altogether more fleshy than his father-in-law's. His work is still relatively unknown, and only a few pictures can be attributed to him with certainty.

Catalogue No. 32

Pietro Muttoni, called Pietro della Vecchia

Venice 1603 – Venice 1678

Pietro della Vecchia was a pupil of Padovanino (q.v.), and as well as being a painter was also a musician and writer. He married a daughter of the painter Niccolò Renieri (q.v.). Pietro's pupilage under Padovanino inspired in him a devotion to Venetian painting of the early Cinquecento. He was famous for his imitations or pastiches of sixteenth-century types, e.g. single figures of warriors and pairs of lovers derived from Giorgione, Lotto and also Romanino, and for these he earned the nickname 'della Vecchia'. Although these pictures seem to have been considered by his contemporaries as deliberate fakes, it is by no means certain that Pietro della Vecchia himself thought of them as such, and it seems just as likely that he regarded them as Baroque interpretations of the Cinquecento style.

In his early works in particular he used paint densely, and in this was influenced by the example of Strozzi (q.v.); but his best paintings date from the 1650s and exhibit a keen sense of compositional arrangement (often based on the example of the Cinquecento: see, for example, No.33 here exhibited), perspective and colour tone. Pietro della Vecchia combined in his work the opposing influences of Padovanino and the Caravaggesque Saraceni (q.v.), who returned to Venice about 1619. Gifted with a rare imagination and sense of fantasy, he produced paintings which in their originality may be described as truly Baroque.

Catalogue Nos.33,34

Antonio Zanchi

Este 1631 – Venice 1722

Zanchi came to Venice when still young. There he was a pupil of Matteo Ponzone, and possibly later of Francesco Ruschi. Of the painters of the preceding century it was Tintoretto who most appealed to the young Zanchi, who also developed, probably under the influence of the Venetian work of Strozzi (q.v.) and Liss (q.v.), a strong sense of colour and rich use of paint. In the late 1650s, with the arrival in Venice of Langetti (q.v.) and Loth (q.v.), Zanchi took up their tenebrist style and his own pictures at this period come particularly close to the work of Loth (see No.44 here exhibited).

Zanchi was also influenced to some extent by the work in the Veneto of the Caravaggisti Saraceni (q.v.) and Le Clerc, and also, to a degree, by Renieri (q.v.). As with Loth, in his later work his palette lightened under the influence of Luca Giordano's Venetian pictures of 1670–90. Zanchi himself exerted most influence on Molinari (q.v.), who took up his compositions and style and transmitted them to the painters of the eighteenth century.

Literature: A. Riccoboni, 'Antonio Zanchi e la pittura veneziana del Seicento', in *Saggi e Memorie di Storia dell'Arte,* V, 1966, pp.53 ff., with catalogue raisonné – here abbreviated as Riccoboni 1966.

Catalogue Nos.44,45

(Right) detail of Liberi No.37

List of Exhibits

Iacopo or **Giacomo Palma,** called **Palma Giovane** *(Biography page 40)*

1. Mars and Venus

130.9 × 165.6 cm. (51½ × 65¼ in.)

Provenance: ?Earl of Northumberland, Suffolk House, 1652, transferred to Petworth by 1671; presented by the Duke of Northumberland, 1838 (Gould 1975, No.1866)

National Gallery

Venus, goddess of love, assisted by Cupid, seduces Mars, god of war. The subject, which was popular in art from the time of the Renaissance, symbolises Strife conquered by Love.

A picture which was probably this one was seen by Richard Symonds in the possession of the Earl of Northumberland in 1652: he called it Palma Giovane, and described it as 'A Venus whole body on a bed and Mars a fat red knave which she pulls down a Cupid pulls off his buskins' (Collins Baker 1912, p.235). No.1 was presented to the National Gallery as Tintoretto, but was catalogued as 'Ascribed to Palma Giovane' in 1929 and was accepted as Palma by Cecil Gould (1975, p.183).

Palma's seventeenth-century biographer Ridolfi mentions 'some Venuses joyfully coloured' among the pictures which Palma painted for the Emperor Rudolf II (Ridolfi 1648, II, p.194); but there is no certain means of identifying No.1 with any of those paintings. The same biographer records a 'Venere in atto di disuelarsi a Marte' (Venus in the act of unveiling herself to Mars) which the artist painted for the poet Cavaliere Marino (b.1569) (p.202). Gould (1975, p.183) has pointed out that this is not an accurate description of the present picture. A drawing by Palma of the same subject in the British Museum (Rinaldi 1973, fig.163) more accurately fits Ridolfi's description of the Marino painting, for which it may well be preliminary, and in it Cupid also removes the buskins of Mars. No.1 bears some resemblance to a signed painting by the artist of *Venus and Cupid in the Forge of Vulcan* at Kassel. The pose of Venus, seen from the back and twisting, recalls Titian's Venus in his *Venus and Adonis,* painted by 1554, of which several versions are known (including one from his Studio in the National Gallery). The Cupid who removes the boot of Mars may be a deliberate echo of Veronese's Cupid who binds Mars and Venus in the painting now in the Metropolitan Museum, New York.

Cecil Gould, who believes Venus's hairstyle to be of a type fashionable in the late 1580s, dates the picture to that time. Stefania Mason Rinaldi has verbally suggested later than that, some time in the 1590s.

Carlo Saraceni *(Biography page 42)*

2. Jacob reproaching Laban for giving him Leah in place of Rachel

28.5 × 35.3 cm. (11⅛ × 13⅞ in.)

Provenance: Vitale Bloch, from whom purchased by Benedict Nicolson, 1954; bequeathed by Benedict Nicolson, 1978

Exhibited: Caravaggio en de Nederlanden, Utrecht and Antwerp, 1952 (not in catalogue); *Artists in 17th-Century Rome,* Wildenstein, London, 1955 (71); *Italian Art and Britain,* R.A., London, 1960 (390); *Konstens Venedig,* Stockholm, 1962–63 (123); *Art Historians and Critics as Collectors,* Agnew, London, 1965 (43)

National Gallery

Referred to in the past as *Jacob and Laban* or *The Meeting of Jacob and Laban,* the subject of the picture has recently been suggested as Jacob reproaching Laban for giving him Leah in place of Rachel (Potterton 1979/1). In return for seven years' labour, Laban promised Jacob his daughter Rachel in marriage, but when the time was run, Laban substituted Rachel's elder sister, Leah, in the marriage bed. In the morning Jacob reproached Laban, who replied that in his country it was not the custom for the younger to marry before the firstborn (Genesis, 29 : 25–26).

The prominent female figure on the left is probably Leah. The well in the background, which is strikingly unusual, gives some clue to the subject, as it is probably intended to represent the one at which Jacob and Rachel first met.

The theme is relatively rare in painting. A picture by the Genoese artist Giovanni Andrea de'Ferrari in the Palazzo Bianco in Genoa (Newcome 1972, fig.40a), which seems to be of the same subject, is called *Jacob promising Laban seven Years of Service*; but it is unlikely that the unhappy figures in No.2 can be engaged in the relatively pleasant duty of arranging a marriage contract.

The attribution to Saraceni has never in recent years been disputed. The background landscape owes much to the work of the Northern landscapists, in particular Elsheimer, working in Rome in the early years of the seventeenth century, with whom Saraceni was in contact. A more specifically Venetian prototype may be sought for the figures, and Palma Vecchio's *Jacob and Rachel* in Dresden has been suggested (Wildenstein 1955, p.86).

A date towards the end of the first decade of the seventeenth century is agreed in all the literature on the picture, including Ottani Cavina (1968, p.28).

Damiano Mazza *(Biography page 39)*

3. The Rape of Ganymede

Octagon enlarged to rectangle,
177 × 186.6 cm. (69¾ × 73½ in.)
The sides of the octagon were originally
about 71 cm. (28 in.) long

Provenance: ?Casa Assonica, Padua,
before 1648; Duca Salviati, Rome,
1664; thence by descent to Colonna,
Rome, 1717 until at least 1783;
purchased from the Palazzo Colonna
by Gio. de Rossi; ?sold by him to
Alexander Day by 1800; purchased
from Day by John Julius Angerstein,
1801; bought with the Angerstein
collection, 1824 (Gould 1975, No.32)

Versions: Heinz Kisters, Kreuzlingen; a
drawing at Windsor (Popham and
Wilde 1949, No.418) is a copy after the
picture exhibited

Engraved: by G. Audran, *c.*1666–69 (Le
Blanc 99); by Domenico Cunego, 1770;
?by J. Outrim.

National Gallery

Ganymede, a shepherd boy and son of Tros, the legendary King of Troy, was of such beauty that Jupiter fell in love with him and, in the guise of an eagle, carried him off to Olympus where he made him his cup-bearer (Ovid, *Metamorphoses,* 10). Here Ganymede is shown, unusually, carrying a bow and is carried on the underside of the eagle and not, as one might initially believe, on its back.

The subject enjoyed some popularity in the art of the Renaissance, and the somewhat similar composition of a *Rape of Ganymede* by Correggio (Vienna) may have been known to Mazza. The unfamiliar theme of Jupiter as an eagle with Mnemosyne, mother by him of the Muses, was treated in Venice later in the seventeenth century by Marco Liberi, the brother of Pietro, in a painting that may have been influenced generally by Mazza (Budapest: Donzelli and Pilo 1967, fig.246). Clark (1966, p.17) has proposed that No.3, which he believes may be after a design of Titian, influenced Rembrandt in his treatment of the theme (Dresden); and that Rembrandt could have known it through some means other than the original.

No.3 was attributed to Titian at least as early as 1664 (Gould 1975, p.140), and in the National Gallery in the nineteenth century it was described by Waagen (1854, I, p.332) as 'without doubt intended for a ceiling . . . an admirable work by the master [i.e. Titian] . . . [who] here has proved not only that he was able, when the subject required it, to draw the figure greatly foreshortened, but that he understood, what is much more rare, how to avoid disagreeable distortions. The effect of the handsome boy, coloured in the fullest golden tone, every part being carefully rounded, contrasted with the powerful black eagle which is flying away with him, is admirable.' The picture was first attributed tentatively to Mazza by Crowe and Cavalcaselle (1877, II, p.459), who suggested that it may have been after a design by Titian. It was called Tintoretto by Holborn (1903, p.34), but given to Mazza by Hadeln (1913, p.252), an attribution which has gained fairly general acceptance (Tietze-Conrat 1945, p.271; Donzelli and Pilo 1967, p.278; Pallucchini 1969, I, p.221; Wethey 1975, III, p.212). It is catalogued as 'Ascribed to Damiano Mazza' by Cecil Gould (1975, No.32). The attribution to Mazza depends on identifying No.3 with the picture described by Ridolfi (1648, I, p.224) which was on a ceiling in a pavilion of the Casa Assonica, Padua: 'Ganymede carried off by the eagle, so natural, believed by its perfection to be by Titian. It can be deduced from this to what level of perfection Damiano obtained. And Ganymede could not feel less honoured by the brush of this excellent artist who painted him so soft and graceful than by the pens of the poets who made him cupbearer to Jupiter.'

The only certain date which may be attached to the career of Damiano Mazza is 1573, for an altarpiece in the church at Noale in the Veneto, which is also markedly Titianesque in style. The dating of his pictures is therefore difficult if not impossible, and one can perhaps do no more than place No.3 broadly around 1575.

Alessandro Varotari, called **Il Padovanino** *(Biography page 40)*

4. Penelope bringing the Bow of Odysseus to her Suitors

195.6 × 236.2 cm. (77 × 93 in.)

Provenance: Monte di Pietà (pawnshop), Rome; purchased from there through Macpherson, 1856 (Wynne 1977, p.2)

National Gallery of Ireland, Dublin

The picture was referred to as *Meleager* when it was in the Monte di Pietà in Rome in 1856, and at the National Gallery of Ireland it has always been called *Artemis appearing to Œneus*. The true subject was identified by Elizabeth McGrath as Penelope bringing the bow of Odysseus to her suitors (Homer, *Odyssey,* 21): when Odysseus had not returned after twenty years, his wife Penelope, prompted by Athene, went to her suitors and said, 'Hear me, ye proud wooers, who have beset this house to eat and drink ever without end since its master had long been gone . . . I will set before you the great bow of divine Odysseus, and whosoever shall most easily string the bow in his hands and shoot an arrow through all twelve axes, with him will I go.' The figure on the left may be intended to represent Odysseus's son Telemachus, and that in the centre Antinous, the chief of Penelope's suitors; axes appear in the foreground.

The subject is exceptionally rare in painting, although it was treated by Primaticcio as one of a cycle in the now destroyed Galerie d'Ulysse at Fontainebleau. It is not impossible that No.4 was also painted as part of a series based on the story of Penelope and Odysseus, although no other paintings from that story by Padovanino have been traced. On other occasions Padovanino also painted unusual subject-matter, for example *Eumanes and Roxane* (Hermitage, Leningrad: Fomiciova 1961, fig.163) and *Cornelia and her Sons* (National Gallery No.70, 'After Padovanino'). The present picture is clearly Titianesque in inspiration, and Michael Levey has suggested that for the prominent figure of Penelope, in profile and holding aloft the bow, Padovanino may have recalled such figures from Titian as the huntress in *The Death of Actaeon* (National Gallery No.6420) and Spain in *Religion succoured by Spain* (Madrid), which could have been known to him through copies or prints. Definite borrowings from Titian for any of the figures, or indeed the composition, are however not easily identifiable.

No.4 is a mature work and may be placed after Padovanino's visit to Rome, whence he had returned to Venice by 1618 (Pallucchini 1962, p.124). The similarity of the figure of Penelope to that of Roxane in the Hermitage painting, datable about 1620, suggests a date in the 1620s.

Alessandro Turchi, also called **L'Orbetto** *(Biography page 43)*

5. The Flight into Egypt

306.5 × 179.5 cm. (120½ × 70½ in.)

Provenance: ?Sidebottom, Harewood Lodge (label on back); St Luke's Church, Cheetham Hill, Manchester (built 1836–39); acquired from there, 1979

Versions: Madrid (284 × 200 cm.: Scaglietti 1974, No.97); S. Pietro Apostolo, Sassoferrato (size unknown: Urbino 1970, p.191, as a copy); Naples (225 × 147 cm.: Longhi 1926, fig.256); private coll., Bologna (235 × 150 cm.: Scaglietti 1974, p.123); S. Lorenzo, Vittoriosa, Malta (size unknown: Longhi 1926, p.292)

City Art Gallery, Manchester

(Photographed before restoration)

The episode of the Flight into Egypt is mentioned only in St Mark's Gospel (2:13–15): an angel appeared to St Joseph and warned him to flee with the Christ Child to Egypt as Herod would seek out the child and kill him.

Pevsner (1969, p.339) thought the picture Spanish seventeenth-century; it was first attributed verbally to Turchi by Ellis Waterhouse.

It is one of several compositions (see *Versions*) which fit a seventeenth-century description by Passeri of an altarpiece in the church of S. Romualdo, Rome (Passeri 1675–79, p.179): 'on the altar right of the entrance; it represents the Flight into Egypt with St Joseph, the Virgin Mary and Christ Child. It shows the Virgin Mother seated on a donkey; she holds her beloved son in her arms and is looking at him lovingly, and clasps him to her breast in an affectionate gesture of love and awe, and an angel who has the air of a wanton and charming youth, wearing a white but soft and slight drapery which flutters in the air leaving his breast and right arm bare; and an angel leads the fortunate donkey by the rein. St Joseph is seen trying to hasten the flight with urgent steps, and to show that they are approaching Egypt a landscape view can be seen in the distance and they are passing an obelisk. The beauty of the colour of this picture is wonderful, and it is easy to remain to examine it more closely, because its effect is extremely pleasant and to tell the truth it deserves some praise for a certain polished charm and the finish of a well executed work which delights even though the taste is not perfect, but it has many aspects worth consideration.'

To the number of versions already known may now be added the present, hitherto unknown, picture. Longhi (1926, p.292) believed the Naples picture, which was bought in Rome for the King of Naples in the eighteenth century, to be the original. That picture is smaller than either No.5 or the Prado version. The latter has also been claimed to be Turchi's prime version (Scaglietti 1974, p.123), but that claim seems to rest solely on the supposition that because the Prado painting was bought in Rome some time fairly shortly before 1788 it must be the original. There is no reliable evidence as to when Turchi's altarpiece was removed from the church. Longhi (1926, p.292) says this happened in the early eighteenth century, although the picture is described as in the church – perhaps unreliably – by guidebooks of the eighteenth century and later, e.g. Lanzi (1822 ed., II, p.158). Zannandreis in his life of Turchi (1891 ed., p.241) mentions the picture as having been painted for S. Romualdo, and describes it, although his description is in fact based on Passeri. The church itself was demolished in the late nineteenth century (Passeri 1675–79, ed. Hess, p.179, n.3). The provenance of the present picture has so far not been established.

The angel is of a type which appears in other paintings by the artist, e.g. *St Agatha in Prison* (Walters Art Gallery, Baltimore), and its probable prototype is Caravaggio's angel in *The Rest on the Flight into Egypt* (Galleria Doria-Pamphili, Rome).

The Prado version has been dated 1635–40 (Scaglietti 1974, p.123); the altarpiece was first described in 1638 (Totti 1638, p.286), and a date shortly before that might seem reasonable.

6. The Deposition of Christ

Panel, 53 × 33.5 cm (20⅞ × 13¼ in.)

Inscribed: Marcus Antonius BASSETTVS VERONENSIS achademicus Faciebat MVNVS (on the reverse)
(Marcantonio Bassetti academician (i.e. painter) of Verona performed this duty)

Provenance: a religious foundation, Barnes, London; Sabin Galleries, London, from whom purchased, 1973

Exhibited: Cinquant'anni di pittura veronese 1580–1630, Verona, 1974 (136)

Private collection

The episode of the Deposition from the Cross is mentioned in all four Gospels: after the Crucifixion, Joseph of Arimathea, a rich man and a disciple of Christ, asked Pilate for the body of Jesus which he subsequently entombed. In St John's Gospel (19:39) we are further told that Nicodemus brought a mixture of myrrh and aloes which he used with linen cloths to bind Christ's wounds, and this is what Bassetti illustrates. The other figures are probably the Virgin Mary, another Mary and St John the Evangelist.

The body of Christ is shown resting on what is intended as the Stone of Unction (a much venerated relic enshrined in the Holy Sepulchre in Jerusalem), a motif which is found particularly in Northern representations of the Deposition, e.g. Rogier van der Weyden's *Pietà* in the Uffizi, Florence, and the *Pietà* from the Studio of the Master of the Prodigal Son in the National Gallery (No.226). It was popular with painters from Venice and the Veneto in the sixteenth and seventeenth centuries, and examples may be found in the work of Cima, Pordenone, Moretto, Barocci and Tintoretto. It is seen also in Caravaggio's so-called *Entombment* in the Vatican.

Scenes from the Passion are fairly common in Bassetti's oeuvre, and other treatments of the Deposition by him include a picture in the Borghese Gallery, Rome, and a sketch at Windsor. No.6 differs from those compositions in that they are more spacious, and the prominence given to the figure of Nicodemus, which introduces a personal and intimate note, is relatively unusual.

In its technique, No.6 is characteristic of Bassetti in his very late phase and Ottani Cavina (1974, p.156) places it at the end of his career, about 1630.

Domenico Fetti *(Biography page 36)*

7. St Barbara

100.7 × 75.6 cm. (39⅝ × 29¾ in.)

Inscribed: with the number 754 which refers to the inventory of pictures at Hampton Court about 1780–86

Provenance: Gonzaga inventory, Mantua, 1627; Charles I; sold during the Commonwealth and recovered at the Restoration; thence by descent (Levey 1964, No.472)

Exhibited: Venetian Baroque and Rococo, Ferens Art Gallery, Kingston upon Hull, 1967 (18)

*Hampton Court
Her Majesty the Queen*

The subject of the picture was identified by Michael Levey (1964, No.472). On the right is part of the tower in which the Saint (according to the *Golden Legend*) was imprisoned by her father in order to discourage suitors.

Two sets of paintings of saints by Fetti, one comprising eight pictures and the other seven, were recorded in the Gonzaga inventory at Mantua in 1627, and Charles I's inventory records fifteen saints by Fetti (Levey 1964, p.78). Of these only twelve, including No.7, are now in the Royal Collection and hang at Hampton Court.

Shortly after his arrival at the Gonzaga court in 1613, Fetti painted a series of six half-length saints for the monastery of S. Orsola, which had been founded by the Duke of Mantua's daughter, Margherita Gonzaga (Paccagnini 1956, figs.313–18). These, one of which is signed and dated 1613, are now in the Palazzo Ducale at Mantua: they are somewhat similar in format though smaller than the Hampton Court saints. The Mantua and Hampton Court series are markedly different in style, and it is perhaps not unreasonable to suggest that the latter were painted under some influence from Rubens, who, between 1600 and 1608, had worked intermittently at the Mantua court. A group of saints by Rubens now in Madrid, while conceivably contemporary with No.7, offers some parallel; and it is not impossible that some similar saints by Rubens remained at Mantua during Fetti's time.

Levey (1964, p.78) has drawn attention to the divergencies of handling between the different saints at Hampton Court, and suggests that they may have been painted at different dates. Fetti was at Mantua from 1613 until 1622. In the treatment of the composition and colour, No.7 is certainly much more mature than any of the Mantua series of 1613, and might perhaps be dated around 1620.

Domenico Fetti *(Biography page 36)*

8. Portrait of Vincenzo Avogadro

114.6 × 90.2 cm. (45⅛ × 35½ in.)

Inscribed: VINCᵒ AVOGᵒ REC. ECCL. S.S.GER.
ET/PROT. MANT. ANNO
N. D.CX(?)/ÆTA. SVE. ANN XXXV
*(Vincenzo Avogadro, rector of the church of
SS. Gervaso e Protaso at Mantua, in the
year 16—[?] in the 35th year of his age)*

Provenance: Consul Smith; purchased
from him by George III, 1762; thence
by descent (Levey 1964, No.470)

Exhibited: The King's Pictures, R.A.,
London, 1946–47 (254)

*Buckingham Palace
Her Majesty the Queen*

The sitter, clearly identified by the inscription, is shown with a crucifix and what may be a prayer book.

The painting, which was sold by Consul Smith to George III as Van Dyck, was first attributed to Fetti in the R.A. catalogue of 1946, and the attribution is accepted by Michael Levey (1964, No.470). Fetti painted an altarpiece, *St Martin in Ectasy,* for the church of SS. Gervaso e Protaso at Mantua (Paccagnini 1956, fig.323), of which Vincenzo Avogadro was rector. From research in the Archivio di Stato at Mantua, Perina (1971, p.17) has established the date of the altarpiece as 1619–20. There is a damage after the letters 'D.CX' in the inscription on the portrait, and it may be that a further digit is missing. It would seem not unreasonable to link No.8 with the *St Martin* altarpiece, and it may confidently be suggested that the missing digit is 'x' and that the date of the portrait is 1620.

9. The Sacrifice of Elijah before the Priests of Baal

Panel, 61 × 69.9 cm. (24 × 27½ in.)

Provenance: ?Gonzaga inventory, Mantua, 1627 (634); Charles I; sold during the Commonwealth and recovered at the Restoration; thence by descent (Levey 1964, No.471)

Exhibited: The King's Pictures, R.A., London, 1946–47 (270); *Seicento a Venezia,* Venice, 1959 (45); *Italian Art and Britain,* R.A., London, 1960 (50); *The Queen's Pictures,* Queen's Gallery, London, 1977 (22)

Hampton Court
Her Majesty the Queen

At Elijah's prayer fire fell from heaven and consumed his sacrifice, whereas the invocations of the priests of Baal had been fruitless (I Kings, 18:38). On the left are Ahab and the worshippers of Baal. The episode was interpreted as an Old Testament prefiguration of the Pentecostal descent of the Holy Ghost.

The subject is rare in painting, although some examples, mainly by Northern painters, are known (Pigler 1974, I, p.176). Of these one might single out an engraving by Maerten van Heemskerck (Hoogewerff 1941–42, IV, p.380, fig.181), which Fetti may well have known, though its composition resembles only in a general way that of No.9. Askew suggests that Fetti's prototype was a woodcut of the subject in an illustrated Bible published at Lyons in 1573 (1976, p.22 and fig.6). She sees Fetti's composition as a modification of that design and suggests also some figural borrowings. The similarity between the pose of Ahab and that of Michelangelo's statue of *Moses,* which Fetti would certainly have seen in Rome, may be conscious.

No.9 is probably the picture which is called a *Sacrifice of Noah* 'di mano del Fetti' in the 1627 inventory of the Gonzaga collection at Mantua (Levey 1964, p.77). It was thought to be by Aert de Gelder in the nineteenth century and was re-attributed to Fetti by Longhi (1946, p.68). Ivanoff (1963, p.40) believes the painting to be a *bozzetto,* but Askew (1976, p.22) has drawn attention to the fact that as no oil sketches can be ascribed to Fetti it seems unlikely that he ever painted any. Furthermore, no large-scale version of No.9 is known.

Longhi (1946, p.68) and Ivanoff (1963, p.40) place the picture in the artist's very late, and to them Venetian, phase, i.e. after 1621. Askew (1976, p.22) suggests 1622. In view of the picture's probable provenance, it would seem more likely that it was painted in Mantua, though it could still be a very late work, of 1620–21.

Domenico Fetti *(Biography page 36)*

10. Portrait of a Man holding a Sheet with Music

174.6 × 128.2 cm. (68½ × 50½ in.)

Provenance: purchased in London before 1772 by the 5th Earl of Carlisle (ms. at Castle Howard); thence by descent

Exhibited: 17th-Century Art in Europe, R.A., London, 1938 (307); *Picture of the Month: Treasures from Yorkshire Houses,* No.25, City Art Gallery, Leeds, 1949

Version: Uzielli-DeMari coll., Genoa (Donzelli and Pilo 1967, p.175; Marangoni 1922–23, illus. p.781)

The Castle Howard Collection

(Photographed before restoration)

The picture was seen at Castle Howard in 1772 by Horace Walpole, who described it as 'a musician by Fetti, very fine' (Walpole 1927–28, p.73). Waagen (1854, III, p.322) also attributed it to Fetti, and thought it possibly a self-portrait. He also described it erroneously as 'to the knees': the portrait is in fact full-length.

The sitter, who is shown in a form of fancy dress or theatrical costume, holds a sheet of paper on which some music is inscribed, and he deliberately indicates an upturned bowl on the ground beside him. To the right in the middle distance a young man, by raising his finger to his lips, indicates silence. Beside this figure there is a pentimento of a figure in a different position.

The identity of the sitter has not been established. It seems certain that a clue is provided by the very definite gesture of his right hand, and the partly completed music must also be relevant. He may be a patron of music, himself a musician, or (most likely) an actor shown in a role from a play. There is a vague tradition that he is the Venetian composer Claudio Monteverdi (1567–1643); but he bears little resemblance to the accepted true images of Monteverdi – an engraving published in Venice in 1644 (Askew 1978, fig.5) and a portrait at Innsbruck attributed to Strozzi (Askew 1978, fig.7). Monteverdi would have been forty-six at the very earliest date by which Fetti, who came to Mantua in 1613, is likely to have known him; and even allowing for the inconsistencies of portraiture with regard to age, the man in No.10 looks younger than that. Michael Levey has suggested that the sitter is probably a dwarf, or deformed, and pointed out that there were dwarfs and buffoons at the Mantuan court under Ferdinando Gonzaga.

The Palladian-Sansovinesque arch with spandrel figures in the background appears also in two of Fetti's parable compositions, *The Prodigal Son* and *The Rich Man and Lazarus.* (For Fetti's parable pictures and their dating see Nos.11 and 12 in this exhibition.) Michelini (1955, p.132) believes in the case of the parables that such architecture indicates that the pictures were painted after Fetti's visit in 1621 to Venice, where he would have seen similar details; but Askew (1978, p.29), who sees the architecture in the parable paintings as less specifically Venetian, and describes it as 'a North Italian 16th-century palace architecture', points out that Fetti would in any case have been familiar with such arches from the work of Veronese, e.g. *The Family of Darius before Alexander* (National Gallery, No.294).

Pamela Askew has kindly drawn attention to an entry in an *Inventoire des Tableaux du Roy . . . dans les appartements de Monseigneur le Duc Dantin, en son hôtel à Paris en l'année 1715* (Archives Nationales, Paris, O'1965) which describes 'Un tableau copié par Stiémart d'après le Fety . . . représentant un homme tenant dans sa main gauche un papier'. This copy by the painter François Stiémart (d.1740) need not necessarily refer to the present composition; and the presence of a *pentimento* in the Castle Howard picture would make it unlikely that it was a copy.

No.10 may certainly be placed at the very end of the artist's short career, *c.*1621–23.

11. The Mote and the Beam

Panel, 61.2 × 44.6 cm. (24⅛ × 17⅝ in.)

Provenance: Casa Grassi, Venice; Grassi sale at Prestages, London, 2–4 Feb., 1764 (32); Samuel Rogers sale, London, 28 Apr. 1856 (chalk date on back but not in sale catalogue); Christie's, 23 May 1924 (73), bt Colin Agnew; F.D. Lycett Green; presented by him, 1955 (York 1961, I, p.19)

Exhibited: Agnew's, London (Magnasco Society) 1924 (6); *17th-Century Art in Europe,* R.A., London, 1938 (295); *The Lycett Green Collection,* York, 1955 (17)

Versions: Princeton University Art Museum; Earl Spencer, Althorp; private coll., Turin (in 1949); Sir Andrew Fountain, Narford Hall, King's Lynn; David Carritt, London, 1978; Busiri Vici, Rome

Engraving: by Pietro Monaco (Le Blanc 198), when No.11 was in the Grassi coll. (Bertini 1949, fig.1)

City Art Gallery, York

The subject of the picture, generally referred to as *The Parable of the Mote and the Beam,* is not, strictly speaking, a parable but rather a proverb or saying of Christ (Trench 1910). It comes from the Sermon on the Mount (Matthew, 7:3): 'And why beholdest thou the mote that is in thy brother's eye, but considerest not the beam that is in thine own eye?'

Fetti shows an old man arguing with a younger, a wooden beam projecting towards the eye of the former with a mote (splinter) from it towards the eye of the latter. The subject is unusual in art, but Askew (1961, p.26, No.22) mentions an engraving after Hendrick Goltzius by Gerard de Jode which shows the same symbolism.

Fetti is known to have painted twelve of the thirty New Testament parables, and, in similar format, two of the sayings of Christ – *The Mote and the Beam* and *The Blind leading the Blind* (see No.12 in this exhibition). Of these fourteen pictures, ten exist in more than one version. Paintings of parable subjects are more usual in the art of Northern Europe, but there was also some tradition of them in Northern Italy, particularly in the sixteenth century. Artists who painted such subjects include Veronese, Jacopo Bassano, Tintoretto and Saraceni. A group of painters from the North of Europe who worked in Rome in the earlier years of the seventeenth century – Elsheimer, Lastman, Pynas and Uyttenbroeck – also painted parables. Fetti could have known examples by all these artists, but of all parable painters he is the one with whom the genre is most associated; and his compositions, always on a small scale and on panel, are particularly original and attractive.

A document of 1631 (Askew 1961, p.23) mentions that various parable paintings by Fetti were to be found placed high up in some small rooms of the Palazzo Ducale at Mantua, where the artist worked. A problem arises owing to the large number of versions of many of the parables; but it may be taken as certain that Fetti sometimes repeated his own compositions and that more than one version of a composition can be by him and need not be the work of an imitator.

No.11 was published by Askew (1961, p.26) as Fetti's second version of the theme, of which the prime is the painting in the Busiri Vici collection, Rome (Askew 1961, fig.4). There are some differences between the two: the physiognomy of the younger man is not the same, and in the Rome painting the older man is not seated but stands, and the urn behind him is much more elaborate. The treatment of the foliage and masonry also varies.

For a discussion of the dating of Fetti's 'parable' paintings, see under No.12 here exhibited. Askew places *The Mote and the Beam* among the parables which she believes Fetti painted between 1618 and 1621, before his visit to Venice.

12. The Blind leading the Blind

Panel, 60.9 × 44.2 cm (23⅞ × 17¾ in.)

Provenance: Dr Bragge sale 1753 (61); bt 3rd Earl of Cholmondley, Houghton Hall; thence by descent; Arthur Tooth, from whom acquired, 1949

Exhibited: Holbein and other Masters, R.A., London, 1950–51 (301)

Versions: Dresden (horizontal format with composition extended to the right); Pinacoteca Nazionale, Bologna; Duke of Northumberland, Alnwick (here exhibited, No.13)

Barber Institute of Fine Arts, University of Birmingham

In likening the Pharisees to blind men, Jesus told His disciples, 'And if the blind lead the blind, both shall fall into the ditch' (Matthew, 15:14).

The picture was published by Askew as an autograph version of a painting by Fetti in Dresden (Askew 1961, p.36 and fig.15). The same writer has pointed out that a painting of the subject by Pieter Bruegel now in Naples was in the Gonzaga collection at Mantua when Fetti worked there. Pevsner (1928, p.156) first drew attention to the fact that the landscape setting of the Dresden version of Fetti's *Blind leading the Blind* was undoubtedly inspired by Veronese's *Good Samaritan,* also now in Dresden.

The Fetti at Dresden, which Askew (1961, p.35) justifiably considers the prime version of the composition, is of similar height but horizontal in format. No.12 is basically a detail of the left hand side of that picture with the landscape background treated differently, showing buildings where the Dresden version has tall trees.

No precise date can be established for any of Fetti's parable paintings, but it is generally agreed that they were painted late in his career, and probably not before 1618. In the summer of 1621 Fetti spent some months in Venice, and Askew (1961) has grouped the parable paintings into those painted at Mantua before that visit, and those painted after his return and before his final settling in Venice by September 1622. She considers No.12 to be a later refinement of the Dresden composition, and includes it among the works which she believes Fetti painted after his return to Mantua, which show 'a new breadth of organisation, a more enveloping atmospheric light and colour, an intensification of mood and a greater scope and freedom of pictorial handling'. It might therefore be placed early in 1622.

13. The Blind leading the Blind

Panel, 60.9 × 30.4 cm. (24 × 12 in.)

Provenance: Cammuccini coll., Rome; purchased from there by the 4th Duke of Northumberland, 1856; thence by descent

Exhibited: Noble Patronage, Hatton Gallery, Newcastle upon Tyne, 1963 (55); *Italian Art 1600–1800,* Bowes Museum, Barnard Castle, 1964 (20)

Versions: see under No.12 here exhibited

The Duke of Northumberland, Alnwick Castle

For the subject and discussion, see No.12.

The picture, which was attributed to Schedone when in the Cammuccini collection, was first given to Fetti by Waagen (1857, p.470). Askew (1961, p.42) lists the painting, which in 1961 had not been cleaned, among the versions of the picture in Dresden. No.13 certainly seems close to Fetti's style, and comparison with the Birmingham version will prove fruitful. Like that version, it can probably be dated 1622.

14. The Parable of the Labourers in the Vineyard

Panel, 62 × 45.1 cm. (24½ × 17¾ in.)

Provenance: ?Barberini Palace, Rome (Exeter 1954, No.29); recorded at Burghley by 1797 (Burghley 1797, p.57)

Versions: Dresden; Pamela Askew (bt Christie's, 1954); Castelvecchio Museum, Verona; Capitoline Museum, Rome; Palazzo Pitti, Florence; Mrs Alfred duPont, Florida; A. Staring, The Hague; ex coll. Sir Andrew Fountain, Christie's, 1 Dec. 1978 (3); Dublin (here exhibited, No.15)

The Marquess of Exeter, Burghley House

Jesus told His disciples of the owner of a vineyard who paid his labourers an equal wage per day regardless of the length of time they had worked. When those who had worked longest complained, the Lord of the Vineyard replied, 'So the last shall be first and the first last.' (Matthew, 20:1–16)

The Lord of the Vineyard is seated and remonstrates with an old labourer whose attitude of resting on his shovel and torn clothes suggest that he has worked all day. To the right are younger labourers whose fine clothes in good state indicate that they have not worked long. Michael Levey has aptly drawn attention to the fact that the scene is not actually taking place within a vineyard, although the two figures on the left, the one holding a book probably intended as a steward, are possibly at the vineyard gate.

The painting is referred to in the 1954 catalogue of Burghley as from the Barberini collection, Rome, but there is no obvious mention of it in any of the published Barberini inventories (Lavin 1975). It has been at Burghley since at least 1797, but nevertheless is virtually unpublished and is not included in any of the literature on the artist. It was not known to Askew (1961).

Askew (1961, p.39) considers the composition at Dresden the only one which is certainly by Fetti's hand. No.14, like other versions, differs from it in some respects: in Dresden a dog's head is included in the bottom left hand corner; the architecture of the houses on the extreme left is different: there is no protruding beam in the background wall; and the sole of the labourer's shoe is more obviously torn. No.14 is certainly a picture of quality, and its autograph possibilities warrant some consideration in the context of the other parable paintings by Fetti in this exhibition.

For the dating of the parable paintings, see under No.12. Askew (1961) considers *The Parable of the Labourers in the Vineyard* among the compositions which Fetti painted after his visit to Venice in 1621, and a date late in 1621 or early in 1622 may be suggested.

15. The Parable of the Labourers in the Vineyard

Panel, 62 × 39 cm. (24¾ × 15⅜ in.)

Provenance: Thomas Bodkin; presented by him, 1927

Versions: see under No.14 here exhibited

National Gallery of Ireland, Dublin

For the subject and discussion, see No.14.

The picture was published by Askew (1961, p.44) as a 'not very distinguished replica' of the painting in Dresden. Nevertheless, cleaning has revealed its quality to be reasonably high, and it calls for further examination.

There are differences between it and the prime version of the composition at Dresden (as well as between it and No.14 here exhibited). Some of them, such as the torn sole of the labourer's shoe and the absence of a dog in the bottom left corner, are among those found in other versions; but the labourers on the right differ in both feature and dress from those in Dresden. There is also some variation in the treatment of the Lord of the Vineyard's costume, and in his physiognomy and attitude. The differences in the background architecture, foliage and lighting are not just variations, but in fact reveal an alternative approach to the composition. Such distinctive departures may, if anything, suggest the work of Fetti himself rather than an imitator.

Because of the number of versions of Fetti compositions, attempts at establishing provenance must be extremely cautious. For example, No.15 has been tentatively suggested as the picture in the Sir Andrew Fountain sale in 1731 (83), that picture was sold at Christie's on 1 December 1978 (3); and a version in the Bishop of Bristol sale in 1807 need not, as Askew has implied, be No.15.

With No.14 here exhibited, the present version may be dated to late 1621 or early 1622. If it is indeed an original work by Fetti, it might be later than the Dresden composition but earlier than the other versions.

Johann Liss (Jan Lys) *(Biography page 38)*

16. The Fall of Phaeton

128 × 110 cm. (50⅜ × 43 5/16 in.)

Provenance: M. A. W. Swinfen Broun, Swinfen Hall, Lichfield; purchased at his sale, Christie's, 10 Dec. 1948 (76)

Exhibited: Vasari to Tiepolo, Hazlitt, London, 1952 (5); *Unbekannte Schönheit,* Kunsthaus, Zürich, 1956 (156); *Seicento a Venezia,* Venice, 1959 (58); *German Art 1400–1800,* City Art Gallery, Manchester, 1961 (186); *Art Historians and Critics as Collectors,* Agnew, London, 1965 (8); *Deutsche Maler und Zeichner des 17. Jahrhunderts,* Berlin-Charlottenburg, 1966 (44); *Johann Liss,* Augsburg Rathaus and Cleveland Museum of Art, 1975–76 (A.26)

Denis Mahon, Esq.

The picture was called *'The Fall of Icarus* by Albani' at Christie's in 1948, and published with its correct title and attribution by Bloch (1950, p.278). Having persuaded his father, the Sun god Helios, to allow him to drive his chariot, Phaeton lost control of the horses: to prevent the destruction of heaven and earth, Jupiter hurled a thunderbolt, which sent Phaeton tumbling to his death in the river Eridanus (Ovid, *Metamorphoses, 2*). On the left, naiads wail at the drying up of rivers in the intense heat; on the right are the river god Eridanus and, behind him, Phaeton's sisters, the Heliades. The theme was occasionally chosen for ceiling paintings in the Baroque period.

Liss treated the subject on a number of occasions, but only the present picture and drawings at Brunswick (*Liss* 1975–76, No.B.53) and in a private collection (*Liss* 1975–76, No.B.56) are now known. Sandrart (1675, 1925 ed., p.187) refers to Liss as having painted 'in equally brilliant manner . . . the fall of Phaeton, with his chariot, and beneath on earth the water nymphs looking up so terror-stricken with which beautiful nude nymphs, as well as with the graceful landscape and flaming clouds Lys proved that he was a master of colour and charming hues.' Feyken Rijp in his *Chronik van Hoorn* (1709) describes two paintings by Liss of the subject, one owned by the collector Hooft in Hoorn which was some 180 cm. high, the other, 'even bigger', in the Palazzo Pamphili in Rome. A painting of the subject showing Ceres and the Earth on clouds, led by Mercury before Jupiter and appealing to him to remedy the intense heat, was in the collection of Count Algarotti in Venice in 1776 (*Liss* 1975–76, p.187).

No.16 is stated categorically by Bloch (1950, p.282) to be the painting described by Sandrart. This belief is more cautiously expressed in the catalogue of the 1975–76 exhibition (*Liss* 1975–76, p.93), where it is also suggested, as was believed by Steinbart (1958–59, p.192), that it may be the ex-Hooft picture. Attention has been drawn to the fact that it is the earliest example of Liss's preoccupation with landscape painting, and to the apparent influences – particularly in the detail of the meandering mountain stream – of Brill and Poelemburg, both working in Rome and probably known to Liss (*Liss* 1975–76, p.94). Steinbart (1958–59, p.193) suggests the influence of Albani's *Phaeton* cycle in the Palazzo Giustiniani-Odescalchi near Rome, begun in 1609. He also points out that the group of naiads shows some awareness of Bernini's sculptured *Proserpina* of 1622. In the same figures Bloch sees the influence of Cornelis van Haarlem. Within Liss's oeuvre they come closest to a group of figures in *The Toilet of Venus* at Pommersfelden (Steinbart 1958–59, fig.36).

The picture can be placed in the artist's Roman years, about 1624 (*Liss* 1975–76, p.95).

Johann Liss (**Jan Lys**) *(Biography page 38)*

17. Judith with the Head of Holofernes

128.5 × 99 cm. (50⅝ × 39 in.)

Provenance: on the market in Venice, 1914 (*Liss* 1975–76, p.88); Professor Naager, Munich, 1914 (on loan to Alte Pinakothek until 1919); James Dollar, 1919; presented by him, 1931 (Levey 1959, No.4597)

Exhibited: Johann Liss, Augsburg Rathaus and Cleveland Museum of Art, 1975–76 (19)

Versions: Budapest; Ca' Rezzonico, Venice (horizontal format with composition extended to right); Vienna; formerly Italico Brass, Venice (Steinbart 1940, pl.46)

Engraving: by Pietro Monaco, 1739, of the composition (*Raccolta* 1743, I, pl.4)

National Gallery

For the subject see No.24.

Although the composition had been engraved as 'after Liss' in 1739, the picture was once called 'Fetti', and was first formally attributed to Liss by Oldenbourg (1914, p.150). Any doubts which may have existed regarding its status among the various *Judiths* by or attributed to Liss (see *Versions*) were dispelled by the 1975–76 exhibition, when three of the versions were also shown: No.17 emerged clearly as a prime and exquisite original by Liss and superior in quality to the other pictures.

Several models for Liss's treatment of the theme, by Rubens, Artemisia Gentileschi, Pordenone and Guido Reni, have been suggested (Steinbart 1940, p.119 and *Liss* 1975–76), although none would seem to have influenced him in more than the most general way. A lost *Judith* by Rubens known through an engraving (Hollstein 31: *Liss* 1975–76, fig.103) shows the maid from behind, like Liss's *Judith,* and Holofernes tumbling forward out of the composition; Artemisia Gentileschi's contemporary *Judith* (Palazzo Pitti, Florence: Moir 1967, fig.128), and other paintings of the theme by her, as well as a *Judith* from the circle of Pordenone (Steinbart 1940, fig.54) also emphasise a figure seen from behind; and Guido Reni's turbaned female figure in the fresco of *St Andrew led to Martyrdom* in S. Gregorio a Celio, Rome, has been cited in comparison. The pose of Holofernes and the prominence given to his severed neck find some precedent in Veronese's *Judith* (Palazzo Rosso, Genoa) and also in an engraving of *Judith* by Hans von Aachen (Donzelli and Pilo 1967, pl.16, p.405).

The picture is generally thought to have been painted about 1625, when Liss was still in Rome and under the influence of Caravaggio and his followers.

Bernardo Strozzi, sometimes called **Il Prete Genovese** or **Il Cappuccino**
(Biography page 42)

18. Portrait of an Old Man

127 × 101.6 cm. (50 × 40 in.)

Provenance: Julius Weitzner, London; Herner Wengraf, London, from whom purchased, 1971

City Museums and Art Gallery, Birmingham

The sitter is unknown. He is called 'a Genoese nobleman' at Birmingham, but although he is probably Genoese there is no certain means of identifying him as noble. He wears an informal fur-lined cloak. The clock on the table is undoubtedly real, and is of a type described as a tower or belfry clock. It is likely to be German and slightly earlier in date than the portrait (information from Claud Blair). From the Renaissance onwards, clocks were frequently included in portraits (see, for example, National Gallery No.6448 by Murillo), and they were no doubt intended to illustrate the permanence of the painted image in contrast to the transience of life itself. The red curtain is different in both colour and technique from other reds in the picture, and may well be a later, even if near-contemporary, addition.

In pose and physical appearance the sitter bears a coincidental, though nevertheless striking, resemblance to Van Dyck's famous full-length portrait of Cardinal Bentivoglio (Palazzo Pitti, Florence), painted in Rome in 1623 after Van Dyck had visited Genoa.

Mortari (1962, p.24) places the picture very early. She compares it with the *Deposition* in the Accademia Ligustica, Genoa (Mortari 1966, fig.80) and *The Penitent Magdalen* in the Palazzo Bianco (1966, fig.132) and dates it between 1610 and 1615.

Bernardo Strozzi, sometimes called Il Prete Genovese or Il Cappuccino
(Biography page 42)

19. Design for a Basin

Diameter 74.3 cm. (29¼ in.)

Provenance: 'A gentleman' (Sir George Donaldson) sale, Christie's, 22 July 1922 (14), bt Hughes; H.M. Calmann; purchased from him, 1969 (Macandrew 1971, p.4, n.1)

Ashmolean Museum, Oxford

As Macandrew has suggested (1971, p.8) the painting is not an actual design for a basin but rather a painted *concetto,* from which a careful working drawing would have been made. A silver basin in an Italian private collection (Macandrew 1971, fig.2) is evidently derived from the painting, though it differs in some details.

The picture, which was sold in 1922 as *Design for a Shield* by Schiavone, was purchased in 1969 as Strozzi and the attribution has not been doubted.

The design incorporates scenes from the story of Antony and Cleopatra as told in several sources, including Plutarch's *Lives* and Pliny's *Natural History: top oval,* the meeting of Antony, Octavian and Lepidus; *right oval,* Cleopatra rowed up the river Cydnus in a barge to her first meeting with Antony; *bottom oval,* the banquet of Cleopatra; *left oval,* the death of Antony; *centre,* the death of Cleopatra, holding the asp to her breast. The battle scene in the intermediate circle does not seem to represent any particular battle fought by Antony.

It was not unusual for artists to provide designs for silver- and goldsmiths (see, for example, National Gallery No.1195, by Rubens), and in Genoa itself pieces believed to have been designed by Bartolomeo Biscaino (d.1657) and Lazzaro Tavarone (1556–1641) exist (Macandrew 1971, p.8).

No.19 is, however, the only such design by Strozzi that is known and it is one of the few paintings by him on a small scale. The composition of the battle scene owes much to the battle engravings of Antonio Tempesta (1555–1630), which were widely disseminated, and precise borrowings by Strozzi from these prints have been identified (Macandrew 1971, figs.6, 7).

The picture has been dated to the 1620s (Macandrew 1971, p.7), and its stylistic proximity to Strozzi's *Horatius Cocles defending the Bridge* (Denis Mahon: Mortari 1966, fig.244) has been noted. The *Horatius* is a *bozzetto* for one of the ceiling frescoes in the Palazzo Carpaneto (formerly Centurione) at Sampierdarena near Genoa, which are documented to the years 1623–25, and the present picture has been given the same date.

Bernardo Strozzi, sometimes called **Il Prete Genovese** or **Il Cappuccino**
(Biography page 42)

20. Portrait of a Man, perhaps a Venetian Senator

110.5 × 91.5 cm. (43½ × 36 in.)

Inscribed: ANNO. XXXI MENSI. VIII

Provenance: W. G. Cavendish Bentinck, 1894; thence by descent

Exhibited: Venetian Art, New Gallery, London, 1894 (189)

Private collection

The picture, which was not known to Mortari (1966), was exhibited in 1894 as *Portrait of a Senator* and called by Antonov (1972, p.19) *Portrait of a Senator with a Glove.* Clues to the sitter's identity are provided by the inscription on the paper and the robes in which he is depicted. The inscription could refer to the sitter's age (31 years 8 months), the date of his election as, perhaps, a Senator, or the date of the portrait – August 1631. It is not always easy in portraiture to distinguish with certainty between the various robes of state of the Venetian and Genoese Republics. For example, a famous portrait of the Venetian Procurator Grimani by Strozzi (Mortari 1966, fig.429) shows him in robes which are different from those of the Procurator Canal as painted by Daniel van den Dyck (No.32 in this exhibition). It should be said that within Strozzi's oeuvre the costume depicted here seems similar to that worn in a *Portrait of a Member of the Pallavicino Family* (Mortari 1966, fig.216), which probably shows a Genoese Senator.

Antonov (1972, p.19) also likens No.20 to the Pallavicino portrait, and indeed, seeing a physical resemblance between the two, suggests that the present sitter may also be a member of that family. He believes that the inscription refers to the age of the sitter and dates the portrait to the mid-1620s, while noting at the same time a 'fluidity and lightness which prefigures Strozzi's Venetian phase'.

It is usual in portraiture to give the age of the sitter with the formula 'aetas suae' (see for instance No.32 in this exhibition), and it seems more likely that the inscription here refers to the date of the portrait or of the sitter's election as a Senator (?), which may, of course, be the same. If that is the case, since Strozzi probably arrived in Venice early in 1631 the portrait would be of a Venetian dignitary, and among the very first works that the artist painted in Venice. There is some evidence that he quickly found favour as a portraitist after his move, for a portrait of Doge Francesco Erizzo in Vienna (Mortari 1966, fig.314) may also date from 1631, the year in which the sitter was elected Doge.

G. A. F. Cavendish Bentinck, from whom No.20 was probably inherited, acquired most of his collection (including National Gallery Nos.1377, 3942, 5466, 5467, 1333, 1334, 5841 and 5852) in Venice, and that provenance would point further to the portrait being Venetian in origin.

Bernardo Strozzi, sometimes called **Il Prete Genovese** or **Il Cappuccino**
(Biography page 42)

21. The Baptism of Christ

223.5 × 147.3 cm. (88 × 58 in.)

Provenance: in the family of the present owner perhaps by 1811; thence by descent

Private collection

The episode of Christ's baptism in the river Jordan by St John is told in all four Gospels, and all record the descent of the Holy Ghost in the bodily shape of a dove. St John the Evangelist (1 : 29 ff.) records how, on seeing Christ coming to him, the Baptist said 'Behold the Lamb of God' *(Ecce Agnus Dei).* As was common in the art of the Counter-Reformation, Strozzi shows Christ in an attitude of humility.

The picture, which was brought to our attention by Allan Braham, is newly discovered, and seems indisputedly by Strozzi. Only one treatment of the theme by him is recorded (Mortari 1966, p.217). That picture was once the altarpiece in the third chapel on the right in the church of S. Biagio at Vicenza: Arnaldi (1779) says that this altarpiece, 'with St John the Baptist, who is baptising Christ in the Jordan, and above the Eternal Father, and the Holy Ghost, is by Bernardo Strozza' *(sic).* S. Biagio, which is now the offices of the Automobile Club of Vicenza, remained in use as a church until 1798 (Arslan 1956, p.8). No.21 does not include God the Father, and it seems unlikely from the composition that it was at any stage cut down, so if Arnaldi's description is accurate it cannot be the S. Biagio altarpiece.

The provenance of No.21 is unknown. It is now the altarpiece of a private chapel which was built in 1811–18, and there is some reason to believe that it may have been installed at about that time. On stylistic grounds, the picture would seem likely to date from very early in Strozzi's Venetian period, i.e. soon after 1631. Its most striking similarity is with *Christ and the Woman of Samaria* (No.22 in this exhibition), where the head of Christ is practically identical. That picture, which Mortari (1966, p.144) dates to Strozzi's late Genoese or early Venetian period, is here placed *c.*1632, and a date about that time for the present work seems likely.

Bernardo Strozzi, sometimes called **Il Prete Genovese** or **Il Cappuccino**
(Biography page 42)

22. Christic and the Woman of Samaria

110.5 × 121.9 cm. (43½ × 48 in.)

Provenance: 1st Baron Scarsdale, Kedleston, by 1760, when included in Robert Adam's 'Section of the drawing room' (information from Leslie Harris); thence by descent

Exhibited: Holbein and Other Masters, R. A., London, 1950–51 (333)

Version: Bob Jones University, Greenwich, S.C. (Mortari 1966, fig.275)

Drawings: (both for the head of Christ only) Pierpont Morgan Library, New York; Mr and Mrs François Heim, Paris

The Viscount Scarsdale, Kedleston Hall

Christ rested at a well when a woman of Samaria, an adulteress, came to draw water from it. He told her that whoever drank from the well would thirst again, but whoever drank the water which He would give would never thirst. (John, 4 : 1–30)

The picture has been known as Strozzi since at least the middle of the eighteenth century, and the attribution has never been, and indeed need not be, doubted.

Strozzi treated the subject of Christ and the woman of Samaria on more than one occasion: the present picture, of which a replica exists (see *Versions*); a composition with Christ on the left (Hannema collection, Zwolle: Mortari 1966, fig.311); and a drawing in Budapest which has been attributed to Strozzi showing both figures full-length (Mortari 1966, fig.473). The relationship between all three treatments and Palma Giovane's painting of the same subject in the Museo Civico, Verona (a replica of which is in the Palazzo Bianco, Genoa), has been commented upon (Fenyo 1958) – although how or when Strozzi would have known the Palma has not been explained. In pose Strozzi's Christ is generally similar to Palma's, and the two compositions are not unlike. Mary Newcome has drawn attention to drawings which relate specifically to the head of Christ in No.22 (see *Drawings*).

The picture has been dated to Strozzi's Genoese period, i.e. before 1631, by Matteucci (1956) and Fenyo (1958). Mortari (1966, p.144) believes it to have been painted in the artist's last years in Genoa or not long after his arrival in Venice, about 1629–33. A date early in Strozzi's Venetian period, about 1632, seems most likely.

Bernardo Strozzi, sometimes called **Il Prete Genovese** or **Il Cappuccino**
(Biography page 42)

23. A Concert

101.6 × 124.2 cm. (40 × 48⅞ in.)

Provenance: ?Palazzo Sagredo, Venice, 1750; purchased from there by Consul Smith, 1752; purchased from him by George III, 1762; thence by descent (Levey 1964, No.656)

Exhibited: The King's Pictures, R. A., London, 1946–47 (247)

Versions: Galleria Lorenzelli, Bergamo; Dresden; Detroit Institute of Arts; Maggioni coll., Legnano; Cicogna coll., Milan; Leuchtenberg coll., Munich; Museum of Fine Arts, Moscow; Rocchetti coll., Treviso; Binario coll., Rome; Carrer coll., Venice; private coll., New York; Chatsworth; Cobbe coll., Dublin; Musée Massey, Tarbes; private coll., Madrid.

Drawing: a sheet of studies of hands in the Palazzo Rosso, Genoa (Mortari 1966, fig.454) is probably preliminary

Hampton Court
Her Majesty the Queen

The instruments have been identified by Frances Cooper as, from left to right, a tenor shawm, a violin and a lute, the base string of which is being tuned. While the subject is traditionally referred to as a concert, the two musicians are in fact in the process of tuning their instruments, probably at the direction of a third person not shown.

The picture, which until recently has been relatively neglected, appears indisputedly the finest among the very numerous versions of the composition (see *Versions*). Although most have at some stage been published as 'Strozzi', the vast majority would seem to be no more than copies of a popular composition, having little to show of Strozzi's highly distinctive technique, with excessively rich impasto.

Other music-paintings by Strozzi show pipers (Mortari 1966, figs.145, 147, 152, 154). The earliest were probably painted in Genoa about 1615 and show some evidence of Flemish influence. Those pictures have a jolly 'low-life' quality which is quite alien to the spirit of No.23, where the figures have a serious purposefulness as they tune their instruments. The difference in age between the two men is marked, and it is possible that Strozzi intended this to make some point.

The drawing in the Palazzo Rosso has not previously been linked with No.23. Mortari proposes it in general for musical angels in any number of paintings, presumably for instance *The Vision of St Francis* (Brass collection, Venice: Mortari 1966, fig.336). But studies of hands on the sheet are close to the two centre hands of No.23, and a third, although different in pose from the extreme right hand here, shows a hand tuning by twisting a peg.

The subject is one that is associated in particular with Venetian painting: examples are Titian's *Concert* (Palazzo Pitti, Florence), where one of the figures also wears a plumed hat, and, less familiar, National Gallery Nos.2903 and 3 (Venetian School, 16th Century, and Imitator of Titian). It seems therefore probable that Strozzi first painted the composition at some time after his move to Venice in 1631; and Michael Levey (1964) has suggested a date about 1635.

Bernardo Strozzi, sometimes called **Il Prete Genovese** or **Il Cappuccino**
(Biography page 42)

24. Judith with the Head of Holofernes

138 × 98.2 cm. (54¼ × 39 in.)

Provenance: ?Lady Sunderland sale 1749/50 (21); bt Guise; bequeathed by him, 1765 (Byam Shaw 1967, No.217)

Exhibited: Masterpieces from Christ Church, Liverpool, 1964 (43)

Versions: formerly Bob Jones University, Greenwich, S.C. (Antonov 1972, fig.7); another on the market in Vienna, 1959 (Antonov 1972, p.21, n.9)

Christ Church, Oxford

When her city was besieged by the Assyrians, the Jewish heroine Judith pretended to desert her people and, accompanied by her maid, visited the enemy general, Holofernes, in his tent. Alone with him, she decapitated him and then carried his head back in a sack provided by the maid. The Assyrians, alarmed by the loss of their leader, lifted the siege and fled. (Apocryphal Book of Judith, 13 : 8–10)

Bought as 'Italian' in 1750, the painting was attributed in the 1833 catalogue of Christ Church to 'Il Prete Genovese', but the nickname was identified wrongly as Ippolito Galantini. Catalogued by Borenius in 1916 as Strozzi (1916, p.69), the picture is not included in Mortari (1966), although the attribution need not be doubted.

In his poem *La carta del navegar pitoresco* (1660) Boschini described a *Judith* by Strozzi in the Casa Bonfadina, Venice, as follows:

> Giudit la bela Ebrea, la generosa,
> Che per la Patria e per servir a Dio,
> Ardisse con el cuor invigoroso
> De far impresa cusi gloriosa
> Pur del Prete medemo e questa ancora . . .

In addition to No.24, Strozzi treated the subject of Judith and Holofernes in one other composition, of which several versions exist (at Pommersfelden and elsewhere: Mortari 1966, figs.394, 395, 398, 400). That Titianesque composition shows Judith as younger, and is quite different from the present picture. The painting formerly at Bob Jones (see *Versions*) is, though bigger overall (54 × 43.5 cm.), a slightly cut down version of the present composition, and in illustration appears rather harder in technique. Strozzi used a similar scheme of a three-quarter-length figure against a blank background for paintings of comparable subjects, e.g. *David with the Head of Goliath* (Dresden and Cincinnati: Mortari 1966, figs.371,377) and *Salome with the Head of St John the Baptist* (Berlin-Dahlem: Mortari 1966, fig.409). No.24 comes closest to the Berlin painting in composition.

The picture belongs to the artist's Venetian period. The Berlin *Salome* may date from the early 1630s, and Antonov (1972, p.20) suggests a date of about 1635 for the Bob Jones version. A similar date, in the mid-1630s, might also be proposed for No.24.

Bernardo Strozzi, sometimes called **Il Prete Genovese** or **Il Cappuccino**
(Biography page 42)

25. A Personification of Fame

106.7 × 151.7 cm. (42 × 59¾ in.)

Provenance: ?Ferdinando Carlo Gonzaga, Duke of Mantua, Venice, 1709 (Levey 1971, No.6321); Manfrin, Venice, by 1856 and until at least 1872; English private coll. by 1930s; Malcolm Waddingham, from whom purchased, 1961

National Gallery

Fame holds a trumpet and a tenor shawm similar to that in Strozzi's *Concert* (No.23 in this exhibition). The representation of Fame as a winged female figure holding a trumpet is traditional, and the concept of the dual nature of Fame, honourable and dishonourable, being suggested by two different 'trumpets' is not unusual. Frances Cooper has pointed out that the tube of the trumpet, being no more than about 60 cm. long, is much too short, and that trumpet tubes were in general about 185–215 cm. long and curled. If blown, this trumpet would make 'no more than one or two raucous sounds of the hunting-horn variety'. The shawm would make a sweet sound. It seems therefore probable that the shawm is intended to represent honourable fame; the gilded trumpet, dishonourable.

The picture is recorded as Strozzi in the Manfrin catalogues of 1856 and 1872, but it is said to have been later called Tiepolo and then verbally re-attributed to Strozzi by Borenius (Levey 1971, p.211).

Though a relatively simple single-figure composition, the painting has all the richness of colour applied very densely which one associates with Strozzi's Venetian period, and a date about 1635–36 is generally accepted as likely.

Bernardo Strozzi, sometimes called **Il Prete Genovese** or **Il Cappuccino**
(Biography page 42)

26. Personifications of Summer and Spring

72 × 128 cm. (28¼ × 50⅜ in.)

Provenance: Alessandro Aducci, Rome; purchased from him by Richard, 6th Viscount Powerscourt, 1836 (Powerscourt 1903, p.53); Harris & Sinclair, Dublin, 1924, from whom purchased in that year

Exhibited: Holbein and Other Masters, R. A., London, 1950–51 (402); *Seicento a Venezia,* Venice, 1959 (81)

National Gallery of Ireland, Dublin

Referred to as *Summer and Autumn* since its acquisition by the National Gallery of Ireland, the picture in fact shows Summer and Spring, and was called *Primavera e Estate* at Powerscourt (Powerscourt 1903, p.53). Traditionally Spring carries flowers and has garlands in her hair, while the attributes of Summer are corn and fruit.

It is reasonable to suppose that the picture was painted as one of a pair of overdoors representing the four seasons. A record of its original location has not been found and its probable pendant, which would have shown Autumn and Winter, seems lost.

Single half-length female figures by Strozzi are not unusual, but in format, size and composition No.26 resembles such pictures as the two pairs of male saints at Corsham (Mortari 1966, figs.360,364), and indeed it is not difficult to see these women as saints – Spring, eyes heavenward, holding a sprig of flowers instead of a martyr's palm. The types depicted are similar to those which the artist painted late in his career, e.g. *Fame* (No.25 in this exhibition) and the Madonna in *The Annunciation* (Budapest: Mortari 1966, fig.433). A drawing of a female head in the Suida Manning collection (Mortari 1966, fig.475) is not unlike the head of Summer.

A date towards the end of the 1630s, by which time Strozzi, who had worked in Venice from 1631, had absorbed fully the lessons of Venetian colour and light, is generally proposed for the picture.

Bernardo Strozzi, sometimes called **Il Prete Genovese** or **Il Cappuccino**
(Biography page 42)

27. Portrait of a Venetian Gentleman

125.7 × 95.2 cm. (49½ × 37½ in.)

Provenance: Willis sale, 15 Dec. 1915; bt Buttery; Hon. Mrs Ronald Greville, 1916; bequeathed by her, 1942 (Gore 1964, No.47)

The National Trust, Polesden Lacey

The sitter has not been identified. At Polesden Lacey he is called, presumably on account of his costume, *A Cavalier* (Gore 1964, No.47), but, as Aileen Ribeiro has pointed out, his dress was usual in seventeenth-century Venice, and is similar to that worn by several of Strozzi's other sitters (Mortari 1966, figs.388, 391, 402). The swagger, indeed arrogance, of the pose is consistent with Baroque portraiture and resembles the stance of the sitter in Strozzi's *Portrait of a Gentleman* in Dublin. Surprisingly, it seems not to have any obvious prototype in the work of Titian, Rubens or Van Dyck.

Mortari (1966, p.102 and fig.402) compares No.27 with a *Portrait of a Gentleman* in the Palazzo Widmann-Foscari, Venice, which she dates about 1635. It is perhaps closer to a portrait possibly showing Ludovico de Rabatta (Mortari 1966, fig.391), who in 1638 came to Venice where his father was Imperial Ambassador. A date towards the end of the 1630s seems most likely.

Ermanno Stroiffi *(Biography page 42)*

28. Madonna and Child with SS. John the Baptist, Francis and James the Great

106 × 67 cm. (41¾ × 26⅜ in.)

Provenance: Colnaghi, 1963, from whom purchased

Exhibited: Paintings by Old Masters, Colnaghi, London, 1963 (22)

Ashmolean Museum, Oxford

The picture was exhibited in 1963 as Luca Giordano, and identified then by Voss as a *modello* for an altarpiece by Stroiffi in the church of S. Maria dei Derelitti, called the Ospedaletto, in Venice (Donzelli and Pilo 1967, fig.418). The altarpiece, which is signed falsely by another hand and dated 1625, shows the Virgin and Child enthroned, with SS. John the Baptist, Francis and James the Great (who is shown with a pilgrim's staff). It is recorded as Stroiffi in various guidebooks, including Boschini (1664, p.212) and Zanetti (1771, p.378).

No.28, while undoubtedly the *modello* for that altarpiece, differs from it in certain details. In the altarpiece there are extra figures, including angels who hold a crown above the head of the Virgin, another angel between her and St Francis, and a small boy above and to the left of the head of the Baptist. The Baptist's left leg is positioned differently and there is no lamb in the foreground. In the *modello* Stroiffi indicates a Renaissance-type surround for the altarpiece, which is not the one that frames it in the church.

Paintings by Stroiffi are relatively rare. The Ospedaletto altarpiece comes fairly close to the work of his teacher, Strozzi (q.v.). A date early in the 1640s has been proposed for the altarpiece (Donzelli and Pilo 1967, p.380), and it follows that No.28 would also date from that time.

Niccolò Renieri (Nicolas Regnier) *(Biography page 41)*

29. The Suicide of Sophonisba

131.4 × 167 cm. (51¾ × 65¾ in.)

Provenance: Turner Newcomen, Kirkleatham Hall, Yorks.; Kirkleatham Hall sale, Sotheby's, 23 Mar. 1949 (28); bt Wiggins, from whom purchased, 1949

Versions: Gemäldegalerie, Kassel; formerly Walter Chrysler (*Venezia* 1959, No.87), sold Christie's, 1975; Villa Camerini, Piazzola (Voss 1924, illus. p.128)

Leicestershire Museum and Art Gallery, Leicester

At the time of the Second Punic War Sophonisba, the daughter of a Carthaginian general, married a prince of Numidia (which was allied to Rome) and thus won him over to the Carthaginian cause. When her husband was overthrown, his captor Masinissa fell in love with Sophonisba, and, rather than risk her captivity in Rome, sent her a cup of poison which she drank (Livy, *History of Rome,* 30 : 12–15). The subject was extremely popular with painters in the seventeenth century. Sophonisba's crown as princess of Numidia is on the table; the shell-like vessel appears in several other paintings by Renieri.

Sold at Sotheby's in 1949 as 'Domenichino', the picture has been attributed to Renieri at Leicester almost since acquisition and is included in Fantelli's catalogue raisonné (1974/1, No.41) as a version of the ex-Chrysler and Kassel pictures (see *Versions*). The ex-Chrysler painting is the prime version. No.29 comes close to it in quality, but in composition it is closest to the Piazzola version, although in that picture the head of the old maid is different. The picture at Kassel seems almost certainly a copy, albeit contemporary. Fantelli (1974/1, p.269) suggests that it is by one or other of Renieri's daughters, who were also recorded as painters. In the ex-Chrysler picture the background column rises above the head of Sophonisba; the turban of the old maid is different, as is the table. There is also some variation in the folds of the draperies.

A painting by Renieri of Sophonisba as a single figure, crowned and in profile, holding the cup of poison, is in the Museo Civico at Padua (Fantelli 1974/1, fig.29). Renieri repeated exactly the figure of the weeping handmaiden as Tamar in *Amnon and Tamar* at Stuttgart (Ivanoff 1965/1, fig.8c). The physical type of the old maid with darkened skin is found in other Venetian Seicento pictures: see, for example, No.24 by Strozzi here exhibited.

Hermann Voss (1924) first drew attention to the fact that Renieri was influenced to some extent by Guido Reni. The facial type of Sophonisba certainly reflects Reni, although translated by Renieri into his own very distinctive style. The composition, with three-quarter-length figures placed right in the foreground, is more Caravaggesque in origin. The landscape background suggests the world of the Veneto.

No.29 dates from Renieri's full maturity, and Fantelli (1974/1, p.86) suggests a date towards the end of the 1650s, roughly contemporary with the other two paintings by the artist in this exhibition.

30. The Penitent Magdalen

186 × 120 cm. (73¼ × 47¼ in.)

Provenance: Count Vitturi, Venice, 1774; Thomas Moore Slade until *c.*1791; purchased from him by the 4th Earl of Darnley, Cobham Hall (Buchanan 1824, I, p.329); thence by descent; Cobham Hall sale, 22 July 1957 (329); bt Agnew, from whom purchased, 1958

Exhibited: Seicento a Venezia, Venice, 1959 (88)

Versions: (in half-length) private coll., Prague, 1971; Dublin; Palazzo Durazzo Pallavicini, Genoa

City Museums and Art Gallery, Birmingham

St Mary Magdalen is depicted as the traditional penitent figure, long-haired, reading from a book, with a cross and skull. The representation was particularly popular during the Counter-Reformation, as it encouraged devotion to the Sacrament of Penance. The contemplation of death (indicated by the skull) as a spiritual exercise was recommended in Jesuit teaching. The jar is also the traditional attribute of the Magdalen, being associated with the ointment which she used to anoint Christ's feet.

Attributed to Renieri by Buchanan in 1824 (I, p.329), the picture was seen by Waagen (1854, III, p.21) at Cobham Hall where it was called 'Niccolò Regnari', and was described by him as a 'Magdalen reading holding a scroll, a whole length figure of much merit [which] I am inclined to attribute to Marc Antonio Franceschini'. It was listed by F.G. Stephens as Renieri in 1877 (p.10) and sold in 1957 as 'G. Franceschini'. It should perhaps be remarked that although the attribution to Renieri has never recently been questioned, the painting is not as fully consistent with Renieri's style as the other two paintings by him exhibited here. It is the only known full-length among the representations of the Magdalen ascribed to Renieri (see *Versions*). A *Magdalen* by him in Detroit is a different composition and does not show the same model. It is also probably earlier than the present picture. A small early *Magdalen* by Renieri is in the museum in the artist's home town of Maubeuge (Ivanoff 1965/1, p.21, n.1). A further painting of the Magdalen of about the same date as No.30 shows her half-length, holding a skull with both hands and facing right (collection unknown: Fantelli 1977, fig.60). He is also known to have copied 'a large picture' of the Magdalen by Caravaggio, the present location of which seems unknown. That painting and Renieri's copy were both in the collection of Caravaggio's patron, Vincenzo Giustiniani, in 1638 (Salerno 1960, p.101).

A comparison of No.30 with a full-length of the Magdalen by Guido Reni of about 1615 (Galleria Nazionale, Rome) is instructive. Renieri's Magdalen has the same physical appearance as Reni's, and in both pictures she adopts a languid pose with one foot protruding from beneath her skirts. Reni shows her similarly holding a skull, although in his picture she is not the contemplative Magdalen, but instead raises her eyes to a vision of heaven indicated to her by putti. In Reni's composition she is seated in an open landscape.

The Birmingham picture is generally placed in Renieri's Venetian period, i.e. after 1625 (*Venezia* 1959, p.57), and this seems correct. Fantelli (1974/1, p.86) justifiably compares it with the *Sophonisba* and *St Sebastian* here exhibited (Nos.29 and 31) and places it in the 1650s.

Niccolò Renieri (Nicolas Regnier) *(Biography page 41)*

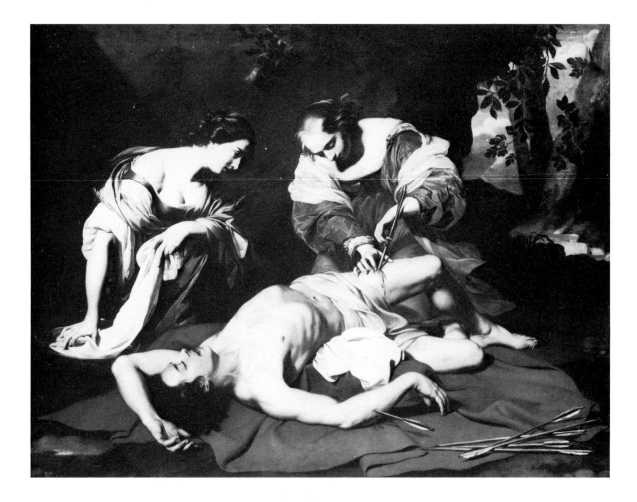

31. St Sebastian attended by St Irene

170.8 × 219 cm. (67¼ × 86¼ in.)

Provenance: Cardinal Fesch (1841 cat., 825); Fesch sale (George cat., 1845, pt 4, 706), bt Aducci; ?Henry Barnard of Cave Castle, Yorks; E.W. Drury; bequeathed by him, 1925

Exhibited: Primitives to Picasso, R.A., London, 1962 (55)

Ferens Art Gallery, Kingston upon Hull

According to legend St Sebastian, an officer in the Praetorian Guard at the time of Diocletian, was discovered to be a Christian, and ordered to be shot with arrows (the scene most usually depicted in the art of the Renaissance). He survived the ordeal, and was discovered by St Irene who removed the arrows. This episode, emphasising as it does the more humane aspect of the story, became popular in the period of the Counter-Reformation.

When in the collection of Cardinal Fesch the picture was called 'French School'; it appeared in the Fesch sale as 'F. Gentileschi' and was bequeathed to Hull as 'Gentileschi'. It was then exhibited in 1962 as Renieri, an attribution which is clearly correct and has not been disputed.

Some paintings of St Sebastian by Renieri (e.g. in Dresden and Milan) show the Saint alone, standing and shot with arrows. *St Sebastian attended by St Irene* at Rouen (*Valentin et al.* 1974, No.74) is similar to No.31, though by no means identical, with the Saint depicted in a pose which is almost the reverse of that seen here. Renieri's *Hero and Leander* at Melbourne (Hoff 1961, p.122) shows Hero as an almost nude, reclining, and prominent foreground figure resembling St Sebastian in No.31.

It seems reasonable to suggest that Renieri's source for these figures was Ribera, whose work he would have seen in Rome. Two paintings by that artist of *The Death of Adonis* (Cleveland, and Palazzo Corsini, Rome) depict an Adonis whose physical appearance and pose are markedly similar. The background and overall format, particularly of the Rome painting, also prefigure No.31. Ivanoff (1965, p.16) suggests the influence on Renieri of the Neapolitan Massimo Stanzione, and, particularly for the facial type of the women, this seems entirely appropriate. The female figure in profile in the present picture bears some resemblance to the mourner in Renieri's *Sophonisba* (No.29 in this exhibition), and the damask of St Irene's dress is similar to that in several paintings of his Venetian period, including *Sophonisba* and *The Penitent Magdalen* (No.30).

No.31 certainly seems much later than the *St Sebastian attended by St Irene* at Rouen, which is usually dated about 1625–26 (*Valentin et al.* 1974, p.96). Fantelli (1974/1, p.86) places it in the 1650s, and this seems reasonable.

Daniel van den Dyck *(Biography page 43)*

32. Portrait of Antonio Canal

113 × 98.4 cm. (44¼ × 38¾ in.)

Inscribed: ANTONIUS CANALIS/D.M.PROC.ᵀ A.ᴼ 1647/AETAˢ. SUAE. 81
(Antonio Canal, Procurator [of St Mark's] in the year 1647. His age 81)

Provenance: Oliver Vernon Watney, Cornbury Park; by descent to his daughter; Agnew's, from whom purchased, 1958

Exhibited: Seicento a Venezia, Venice, 1959 (90)

City Museums and Art Gallery, Birmingham

The sitter is Antonio Canal di Giovanni (1567–1650), who on 9 November 1647 was made a Procurator *di Citra* of St Mark's (Cicogna 1853, p.138). He is shown in the red robes and stole of a Procurator, his coat-of-arms on the left.

The picture, which is not included in the 1915 catalogue of the Watney collection, is called 'Italian 17th Century' at Birmingham (Birmingham 1960, p.82). It was attributed to Daniel van den Dyck by Fiocco (Ivanoff 1959) and exhibited at Venice in 1959 as Renieri. Opinion over the attribution remains divided: Pallucchini and Ivanoff favour Van den Dyck (Fantelli 1974/1, p.93), as do Donzelli and Pilo (1967, p.407); Fantelli (1972, p.160 and 1974/1, p.93) gives it to Renieri. The painting of the flesh and drapes, however, seems quite unlike Renieri at any period, not least his Venetian phase, when his style was brilliantly hard and metallic (compare No.31 in this exhibition).

A group of portraits at Bergamo painted when Van den Dyck was very young, before his move to Venice in 1634, show some affinity with No.32, and demonstrate that he was already then a portrait painter of talent (Ivanoff 1954, figs.266 and 270). The present work is dated 1647, placing it in his Venetian years, when he came under the influence of Renieri.

Pietro Muttoni, called **Pietro della Vecchia** *(Biography page 44)*

33. Timoclea brought before Alexander

188 × 238 cm. (74 × 94 in.)

Provenance: Monte di Pietà (pawnshop), Rome; purchased from there through Macpherson, 1856 (Wynne 1977, p.2)

National Gallery of Ireland, Dublin

Timoclea, a matron of Thebes, was raped by one of the soldiers of Alexander the Great when the latter invaded her city. The soldier then asked Timoclea if she knew of any money concealed. She replied that she did, and showed him a well into which she said she had thrown her valuables upon the taking of the city: when the soldier looked into the well, she pushed him in and then stoned and killed him. Alexander summoned her before him, but she so impressed him by her resourcefulness and dignity – as well as by her declaration that her brother had been killed in the service of his father – that he allowed her and her children their freedom. (Plutarch, *Lives,* 33:12)

The subject is not common in art, and although themes of clemency are familiar in Venetian painting the story of Timoclea is rarely represented. A picture by Domenichino in the Louvre presents the story as one would expect, with Timoclea led in to Alexander. It should be remembered that Pietro della Vecchia was an original, intelligent, and above all extremely witty painter, and his treatment of the theme is, like other paintings by him, intentionally irreverent.

The picture, which is virtually unknown, was attributed to Pietro della Vecchia in Rome in 1856, and this attribution need not be doubted. Another painting by Pietro della Vecchia showing Alexander depicts the episode of Alexander and Diogenes. That work, which is slightly larger than No.33 (212 × 251 cm.: *Venezia* 1959, No.105), was formerly in the Palazzo Widmann-Foscari in Venice. The two paintings, related in composition as well as in subject-matter, may well be pendants. Timoclea's stance is similar to that of Alexander in the Venice picture; the child on the right is included in both, and in both the centre is occupied by a secondary figure.

In treating the story of Alexander, Pietro della Vecchia makes conscious references in both pictures to the most famous of all Venetian 'Alexander' pictures, Veronese's *Family of Darius before Alexander* (National Gallery, No.294). Features in common are the composition, on a platform set against a backdrop, the pose of Timoclea, which resembles that of the principal figure in red in the Veronese, and the conceit of a small boy placed in the corner. Other echoes of Veronese here are the scattered antique fragments and the facial type and pose of Alexander himself.

Veronese's *Family of Darius before Alexander* was in one of the Pisani family palaces in Venice when it was described in 1648 by Ridolfi (Gould 1975, p.321), and Pietro della Vecchia could certainly have known it.

No.33 may be placed in the 1650s, at a time when Pietro della Vecchia had reached his full maturity and produced his best work. Ivanoff (1944–45) indicates a date about 1653 for the *Alexander and Diogenes,* which would also seem likely for this picture.

Pietro Muttoni, called **Pietro della Vecchia** *(Biography page 44)*

34. An Allegory(?)

88.9 × 116.8 cm. (35 × 46 in.)

Provenance: at Burghley by the time of the 9th Earl of Exeter (d.1793); thence by descent

The Marquess of Exeter, Burghley House

The picture is described in the 1797 catalogue of Burghley as *Cupid pulling Fortune by the Hair,* and from 1815 as *Envy plucking the Wings of Youth.* Its precise subject is obscure, but it seems unlikely that the winged female figure represents Cupid, and the identity of the second figure, who may be male or female, is also uncertain, as indeed is the precise nature of the action between them. Elizabeth McGrath has suggested that the picture may illustrate not an allegory but some episode from literature, which would not be unusual for Pietro della Vecchia (see the note on No.40 in this exhibition). She also points out that some contrast between youth and age may be intended. The wings and flowing hair may indicate swiftness, and it may be that the picture represents some action whereby the impetuousness of the youthful figure is being restrained by old age.

The format of the painting, with a strong horizontal emphasis, is typical of Pietro della Vecchia. His chronology is not easy, as throughout his life he worked in a variety of styles. No.34 seems mature work, and a date perhaps about contemporary with his other picture shown here might be suggested, in the 1650s.

Francesco Maffei *(Biography page 39)*

35. The Adoration of the Shepherds

72 × 95 cm. (28¼ × 37⅜ in.)

Provenance: Antoon van Delie (no date); Colnaghi, from whom purchased, 1958 (Ashmolean 1961, No.A922)

Exhibited: Seicento a Venezia, Venice, 1959 (140)

Ashmolean Museum, Oxford

The pillar seen in the background often figures in paintings of the Nativity: it refers to an account by the fourteenth-century Pseudo-Bonaventura, according to which the Virgin arose in the night, leaned against a pillar and gave birth.

An old label on the back of the frame is inscribed 'Giovanni Benedetto', presumably referring to Giovanni Benedetto Castiglione.

A painting of this subject by Maffei was in the collection of Conte Bruno Salsco in 1936 (Ivanoff 1936, p.407), and in addition to the Ashmolean picture at least four other *Adorations* by him are known today: in a private collection at Arcugnano; in the Santuario della Madonna del Castello, Carpanedolo; a painting formerly in the Camerino collection, Venice, which may be the same as that listed by Donzelli and Pilo (1967, p.256) as 'Private collection, Venice' (Ivanoff 1956, Nos.54,55 and p.66); and in the Galleria Estense, Modena (*Venezia* 1959, No.139).

No.35 has certain affinities with all these paintings, mainly in the prominent kneeling figure on the right; but the pictures in Arcugnano, Carpanedolo and Modena are all closer to each other in composition than to it. In his fondness for the theme and his treatment of it, Maffei was inspired by Jacopo Bassano, by whom, or associated with whom, any number of *Nativities* exist. Those in a private collection in Padua and the Barberini Palace, Rome (Ivanoff 1956, Nos.21 and 56) come closest to the present picture.

No.35 is generally placed in the 1650s (Ashmolean 1961, p.91, and Donzelli and Pilo 1967, p.254).

Francesco Maffei *(Biography page 39)*

36. The Annunciation

305 × 150 cm. (122 × 60 in.)

Provenance: probably painted for the Oratory of S. Pietro Martire, Padua (demolished 1822); Palazzo von Haxel, Venice (Hull 1967); private coll., Zürich, 1961 (Pilo 1961/1, No.189d); Agnew, from whom purchased, 1965

Exhibited: Venetian Baroque and Rococo, Ferens Art Gallery, Kingston upon Hull 1967 (36)

Ferens Art Gallery, Kingston upon Hull

This is believed to be the painting of the Annunciation by Maffei that is mentioned in various guides to Padua as being in the Oratory of S. Pietro Martire between at least 1780 (Rossetti 1780, p.51) and 1817 (Moschini 1817, p.157). The Oratory was closed in 1812, and destroyed in 1822 (Pilo 1961/1, p.398, n.31). Another *Annunciation* by Maffei, different in composition, is in the Museo Civico at Vicenza (Barbieri 1962, No.A745).

Pilo (1961/1) has drawn attention to Maffei's dependence on Veronese in this picture, and refers to the Veronese of the same subject in the Accademia, Venice. The flying angel here does have some resemblance to the angel in the Accademia picture; but the figure of the Virgin is derived almost exactly from Veronese's *Annunciation* in Washington, and it is to that picture that the representations of God the Father and cherubs also come closest.

No.36 is characterised by a much less bizarre and quieter mood than many of Maffei's earlier works, in keeping with other pictures of his Paduan period, and a date in the last three years of his life, 1657–60, seems certain.

37. The Finding of Moses

Paper laid on canvas, 46.4 × 64.1 cm.
(18¼ × 25¼ in.)

Inscribed: with inventory numbers 575
and 13

Provenance: Colnaghi, from whom
purchased

Private collection

Pharaoh having decreed that all sons born of Hebrew women be put to death, the mother of the infant Moses hid him in a basket by the bank of the Nile. There he was discovered by Pharaoh's daughter, who rescued him. (Exodus, 2:1–5)

The picture is unpublished, but an attribution to Pietro Liberi seems convincing. A *Finding of Moses* attributed to him is in the American collection of Paul Ganz (Finch 1964, No.25). It is much larger than the present picture, quite different in composition, and shows the later episode of the infant Moses presented to Pharaoh's daughter. No.37 consciously echoes the work of Veronese in both the figure types and the arrangement of the composition, with prominent foreground figures occupying half the picture and the remainder showing a distant view. A number of pictures of the finding of Moses by or associated with Veronese exist, including those in Madrid, Dresden and Washington. In general, No.37 bears some resemblance to all of these, although none has the rather prominent feature seen here, of Pharaoh's daughter pointing. A drawing for *The Finding of Moses* by Veronese (Pierpont Morgan Library, New York: Pignatti 1976, fig.561) does however include this feature, and it is not impossible that there is a lost painting by Veronese which also included it and to which Liberi referred. A *Finding of Moses* by Sebastiano Ricci in the Royal Collection (Levey 1964, No.647), which is a Veronese pastiche, comes closest to No.37, although it is of course later. It includes a negro page, and shows Pharaoh's daughter, as well as one of her handmaidens, pointing. The existence of that painting might argue further for a lost Veronese to which Liberi as well as Ricci referred.

The draperies, with the highlights carefully painted along the folds, are typical of Liberi, and the juxtaposition of two faces, one in shadow, the other in half-shadow, is also usual.

A date some time after Liberi's final return to Venice in 1659 might be suggested, perhaps as late as the early 1670s.

Giulio Carpioni *(Biography page 36)*

38. A Bacchanal

51.1 × 88.9 cm. (20⅛ × 35 in.)

Provenance: Consul Smith; purchased from him by George III, ?1762; thence by descent (Levey 1964, No.430)

Hampton Court
Her Majesty the Queen

All the elements usually associated with a bacchanal are present: bacchantes – female devotees of Bacchus – beating tambourines, satyrs, a drunken Silenus on an ass and a term of Pan. The statue is similar to statues of Venus in other bacchanals by Carpioni, but is here clothed and may not be intended to represent the goddess.

Although undoubtedly by Carpioni and catalogued by Michael Levey as such, the painting is not included in any of the literature on the artist.

Carpioni would have known Titian's work in Venice, and a bacchanal by the latter, *The Worship of Venus* (Madrid), was copied by Carpioni's teacher Padovanino (q.v.). He himself painted bacchanals throughout his career, but no positive chronology had been proposed for them. Dating is difficult: No.38 may perhaps be compared with a *Worship of Venus* at Oderzo (Pilo 1961/2, fig.113) and a *Reign of Hypnos* at Pommersfelden (Pilo, fig.88), both of which Pilo places about 1665.

Giulio Carpioni *(Biography page 36)*

124

39. Belshazzar's Feast

101.6 × 127 cm. (40 × 50 in.)

Provenance: possibly Samuel Madden of Dublin bequest, 1766 (Strickland 1916)

Version: Conte Francesco Castelbarco Albani sale, Sotheby's, Florence, 22–24 May 1973 (266) (103 × 131 cm.)

Trinity College, Dublin

Belshazzar, King of Babylon, held a great banquet for his princes, wives and concubines, at which he used the gold and silver vessels stolen from the Temple in Jerusalem. When the feast was at its height a ghostly hand appeared and wrote on the wall the words 'MENE, MENE, TEKEL, UPHARSIN'. No one could understand the message until the prophet Daniel interpreted it as foretelling the downfall of Belshazzar's kingdom: 'God hath numbered thy kingdom, and finished it. Thou are weighed in the balances, and art found wanting. Thy kingdom is divided, and given to the Medes and Persians.' (Daniel, 5)

In the painting the words are written in correct Hebrew, from right to left. Most other pictures of the subject either do not show the writing or else depict it in Roman script: examples from the Venetian seventeenth century by Celesti (q.v.) in the Villa Mafizzoli at Toscolano and the Palazzo Conti in Padua may be cited (Mucchi and della Croce 1954, figs.30 and 13). Rembrandt in his portrayal of the feast (National Gallery, No.6350) uses Hebrew written vertically from right to left. The banquet, taking place on a raised platform in a pillared hall open to the sky, has some sixteenth-century Venetian prototypes in the work of Titian and Veronese (e.g. *The Feast in the House of Simon the Levi*, Accademia, Venice).

Listed in the 1916 catalogue of Trinity College as 'painted by Phillippe de Champaigne', the picture was first attributed verbally to Carpioni by Sergio Benedetti, who is to publish it. The version, which is identical, is inferior in quality and may be a copy.

Under a cloudy sky, Carpioni contrasts brightly-lit figures or groups of figures with others presented in shadow, and this gives the effect of the costumes being very precisely painted – almost incised. Similar effects are achieved in the paintings which he executed for the ceiling of the Oratory of S. Nicola in Vicenza in 1671 (Pilo 1961/2, figs.168–70); and a date about then, i.e. late in his career, may be proposed for this picture.

40. A Caprice on a Classical Theme(?)

76.2 × 107.9 cm. (30 × 42½ in.)

Provenance: D.F. Beggi, Rome; purchased from him by Henry Davis Pochin of Bodnant, 1872; thence by descent

Exhibited: 17th-Century Art in Europe, R.A., London, 1938 (296); *Seicento a Venezia,* Venice, 1959 (175)

Private collection

The picture has been called *The Temple of Janus,* Janus being the Roman god of doorways and city gates who is usually depicted with two faces. Ivanoff (1958, p.232) called it *The Three Furies* and identified the male figure on the right as Mars, god of war. It may be that the picture depicts some episode from contemporary literature. In Venetian writing of the period there was a certain vogue for burlesques on Classical literature – such as G.F. Loredan's *Iliade Giocosa* of 1651, Pierre Scarron's *Le Virgile Travesti* of 1652 and Ferranti Pallavicino's *La Reti du Vulcano* – and artists of the time, including Daniel van den Dyck (q.v.), Francesco Ruschi and Pietro della Vecchia (q.v.), were employed in illustrating them (Ivanoff 1965/2). Mazzoni himself painted two pictures entitled *The Forge of Vulcan* (Ewald 1960–61, p.139) which Ivanoff (1965/2, p.187) believes may have been influenced by Pallavicino's poem.

Originally attributed to Salvator Rosa, the picture was exhibited as Francesco Maffei at the Royal Academy in 1938. In the catalogue attention was drawn to the similarity between it and *The Death of Cleopatra* at Rovigo (Fiocco 1929/1, illus. p.291), once attributed to Maffei although at that time given to Mazzoni. The attribution to Mazzoni seems to have been first made verbally by Fiocco, and the picture was exhibited as Mazzoni in 1959 (*Venezia* 1959, No.175).

No.40 is among the most extraordinary paintings of an extraordinary painter. The treatment of the architecture is characteristic: it is not used as a backdrop, but as an integral part of the composition, its perspective (see, for example, the floor) enhanced by the action of the figures. Mazzoni was also an architect and may have been a theatre designer as well, and it was by no means unusual for him to employ a low viewpoint in his paintings.

The picture belongs to the artist's full maturity, probably after the dated *Banquet of Cleopatra* in Washington of 1660 (Ivanoff 1958, fig.41), and may be placed about 1665–70.

Giovanni Battista Langetti *(Biography page 37)*

41. The Good Samaritan

137.2 × 108 cm. (54 × 42½ in.)

Provenance: Sir Thomas Holburne (d.1874); by descent to his sister, Mary Anne Holburne; bequeathed by her, 1882

Holburne of Menstrie Museum, Bath

Jesus related the parable of a traveller from Jerusalem to Jericho who, stripped and beaten by robbers, was ignored by a priest and a Levite. When a Samaritan – a Gentile – passed by he bound his wounds and poured on them oil and vinegar (Luke, 10:30–37). Here the Good Samaritan is assisted by two helpers, one holding his horse.

The picture is included in the 1936 catalogue of the Holburne Museum as Luca Giordano, but has since been published as Langetti (Stefani 1966, p.193) which is clearly correct. Three other paintings of the same subject by Langetti are known: in Lyons (Laclotte 1958, fig.1), private collection, Padua (Stefani 1966, fig.233), and Harrach, Vienna (Delogu 1929, fig.6). The picture in Lyons, though horizontal in format and with the composition extended to the right, comes closest to the one exhibited here, which of the four seems the most mature in its solution of the design.

Langetti's interest in anatomy and the influence on him of Ribera and Luca Giordano have been mentioned (Biography, p.37). The profound effect of such compositional and figure types on Carl Loth can be seen, for example, in No.42 in this exhibition.

Langetti settled in Venice in the late 1650s and died there in 1676. No.41 was certainly painted during his Venetian years, possibly around 1670.

Johann Carl Loth *(Biography page 39)*

42. Abraham and the Angels

142 × 168.2 cm. (56⅛ × 66⅛ in.)

Provenance: J. A. D. Shipley, Newcastle; bequeathed by him, 1909

Exhibited: German Art 1400–1800, Manchester, 1961 (185)

Version: private coll., Venice (Ewald 1965, No.22 and pl.51) – perhaps a copy after No.42 by Loth's pupil Daniel Seiter

Shipley Art Gallery, Gateshead

Abraham gave hospitality to three angels, who then prophesied that a son would be born to him and his aged wife, Sarah (Genesis, 18: 1–19). The subject was regarded as the Old Testament prefiguration of the Annunciation, and also, in the period of the Counter-Reformation, when it was most popular in art, as symbolising the third Corporal Act of Mercy, which was to give hospitality to strangers.

The picture was bequeathed in 1909 as Guercino but later attributed to Loth independently by Pignatti and by Ewald, who published it (Ewald 1965, No.21). A painting of the same subject by Loth was exhibited in Florence in 1729 (Ewald 1965, No.23). The pose of Abraham is reflected fairly closely in a painting by Loth at Vienna which is probably later in date, *Jacob blessing the sons of Joseph* (Ewald 1965, pl.48).

The influence of Ribera and Giordano as transmitted to Loth by Langetti (see No.41) is apparent in the picture. Langetti arrived towards the end of the 1650s (Stefani 1966, p.190). A date for No.42 some time fairly soon after the meeting of the two artists might be suggested, possibly about 1660.

43. Mercury piping to Argus

116.9 × 99.7 cm. (46 × 39¼ in.)

Provenance: A. G. H. Ward; presented by him, 1920 (Levey 1959/1, No.3571)

Version: an almost identical composition is recorded in a drawing after Loth at Prague (Ewald 1965, No.407)

National Gallery

Io, loved by Jupiter and transformed by him into a white heifer to avoid Juno's jealousy, was guarded on Juno's instructions by Argus. Jupiter sent Mercury to kill Argus, which he did, having first lulled him to sleep with music. (Ovid, *Metamorphoses, 1*)

Presented to the National Gallery as Liss, No.43 was first attributed to Loth by Fiocco (1929/2, p.43), an attribution which if fully accepted (Levey 1959/1, p.63). A drawing which has been in Prague since at least 1669 (see *Version*) differs only very slightly, mainly in the pose of Argus's left hand, and it is not impossible that it records this painting. A drawing after a probable pendant, showing *Apollo and Pan* in a similar composition, is also in Prague (Ewald 1965, No.368, pl.62).

The marked similarity in type between No.43 and Zanchi's *Seneca and Nero* (No.44) calls for comment. From the time of Loth's arrival in Venice he knew Zanchi. On occasion they collaborated and sometimes they painted pendants to each other's pictures (Ewald 1965, Nos.4, 104), and their work is not infrequently confused (e.g. Ewald, Nos.337, 103, 62). For the present picture Ewald suggests the distant influence of Liss, and also of Langetti.

No.43 is in general dated to the late 1650s (Levey 1959/1, p.63, and Ewald 1965, p.23), and is among Loth's earliest Venetian works.

Antonio Zanchi *(Biography page 44)*

134

44. Seneca and Nero

134.6 × 111.8 cm. (53 × 44 in.)

Provenance: Countess of Bradford, Weston Park, by 1735; thence by descent

Versions: private coll., Milan (100 × 90 cm.); New York art market, *c.*1970

The Earl of Bradford, Weston Park

The Stoic philosopher Seneca was tutor to the boy Nero (who later, as Emperor, was to order his suicide). There was a vogue in the seventeenth century for paintings of philosophers, generally shown as single figures: examples exist by Salvator Rosa, Fetti (q.v.) and, more appropriately for the present work, Ribera, Luca Giordano and Langetti (q.v.). Compositions such as No.44 are, however, more unusual.

The picture was for long called Mola, but on the basis of an entry in *A Catalogue of Pictures Belonging to the Rt. Honble. the Countess of Bradford which were sent from London to Weston in Staffordshire June 1735,* where it is described as 'No.3 *Seneca and Nero* by Carlooch', Garlick (1965, p.1210) re-attributed the painting to Carl Loth. No.44 certainly comes close in style to Loth, and Garlick justifiably compared it with Loth's *Mercury piping to Argus* (No.43 in this exhibition), where the composition and the treatment of light and background are similar. However, a smaller version of the picture which is identical in design (see *Versions*) has been published by Riccoboni (1971, p.265, fig.6) as *A Philosopher with Disciple* by Zanchi, and in illustration appears convincingly to be by that painter. A further version also attributed to Zanchi was on the market in New York in recent years (information from Mr and Mrs Robert Manning).

The close relationship, indeed parallel, between the work of Zanchi and Loth (who arrived in Venice about 1656) has been treated in full by Riccoboni (1966, p.63), who mentions that Fiocco referred to Loth as Zanchi's 'double in manner and technique'. Figures similar to the Seneca here are found in other paintings by Zanchi, including *Abraham teaching Astronomy* in S. Maria del Giglio, Venice (Riccoboni 1961–62, fig.3), and the *Nosce te ipsum* at Hanover (Riccoboni 1966, fig.10). The painting of the book is also characteristic of Zanchi.

Riccoboni (1971, p.265) proposes a date of 1670–75 for the Milan version of No.44. However, in view of the picture's stylistic proximity to No.43 by Loth, which is datable to the late 1650s, a date about that time may also be proposed for No.44.

45. A Scene of Rape

154.9 × 139.7 cm. (61 × 55 in.)

Provenance: Lasson Gallery, London, from whom purchased, 1967

Northampton Art Gallery

The picture is called *The Abduction of Helen* at Northampton: for this subject see under No.50 here exhibited. There are no certain means of identifying the principal figures in the picture as Paris or Helen. Rape subjects are common in Zanchi's oeuvre, and it is not always easy to identify the subject precisely, although pictures which seem definitely intended to show the rape of Helen (Riccoboni 1966, fig.86) usually include some suggestion of a boat and show Paris as youthful and in armour.

Although an authentic painting by Zanchi, No.45 is not generally known and is not included in Riccoboni's catalogue raisonné (Riccoboni 1966). Pictures by Zanchi of related compositions include two now at the Villa Arrigoni degli Oddi at Monselice (Riccoboni 1966, fig.86, and Riccoboni 1971, fig.12), one in the Landesmuseum at Oldenburg, and a painting now lost (Riccoboni 1971, fig.2). Of these, No.45 comes closest to the paintings in Oldenburg, and to one of those at Monselice (Riccoboni 1971, fig.12), in that there too the most prominent figure is also placed diagonally with his head turned sharply and is seen from the back, and an older female figure in the bottom left-hand corner attempts to restrain the action. These three paintings, of which the present picture is the most refined, show a clear progression in Zanchi's rendering of the theme.

The Monselice paintings were described as 'in course of execution' in 1697 (Riccoboni 1966, p.98). No.45 is clearly later than that, and may be placed in the early years of the eighteenth century.

Andrea Celesti *(Biography page 36)*

46. Imaginary Portrait of Count Alberto

206 × 140 cm. (81⅛ × 55⅛ in.)

Inscribed: Albertus De Comitibus/Alberti Filius/Consylvarum Ecclesiam/Proprio aere Construxit/Dotavitque/Et Familiae suae Ius Patronatus reliquit/Idem arrepto Vexllo/Cives ad Libertatem vocavit/Expulso Vrbe Imperiali Vicario/Ideoque Pater Patriae dictus/Mox Consul/Inde post decennium/Praetor creatus est/ANNO D./MCLXXIV

(Albert, Count, son of Albert, built and endowed the Church of Conselve at his own expense and bequeathed the right of patronage to his family. This man, seizing the standard, called the citizens to liberty having expelled the Emperor's representative from the city, and because of this was pronounced Pater Patriae, then Consul, and ten years afterwards was created Praetor. In the year 1174.)

Provenance: Cardinal Fesch; Alessandro Aducci, Rome; purchased from him through Macpherson, 1856 (Wynne 1977, p.2)

National Gallery of Ireland, Dublin

On the basis of the inscription it seems likely that the sitter was of the family of the Counts of Baone who, in 1174, had a castle at Conselve near Padua. Several members of the family bore the name Alberto, and it is recorded that an Alberto da Baone built the church of S. Lorenzo at Conselve (Wynne 1979). A.V.B. Norman has drawn attention to the fact that the armour is fanciful, with some attempt at antiquarianism shown by the besagew (disk) on the left shoulder, the mail shirt and sabatons (shoes).

The picture was purchased as Celesti and, though it is relatively unknown, the attribution has not been and need not be doubted. Portraits by Celesti, who is better known as a subject painter, are not usual. Two portraits similar in size and format, and one of which bears a comparable inscription, are in Ljubljana (Rizzi 1970, p.233). In those paintings the sitters are also depicted in a type of historical armour and hold in the one case a standard and in the other a baton. They also include a putto in the top left hand corner. A further painting of this type attributed to Celesti, described in 1785 as 'Ritratto di uomo vestito di ferro, che tiene nella mano diritta un bastone di comandante' (portrait of a man clad in armour, holding in his right hand a commander's baton) and also bearing an inscription identifying the sitter as 'Count Alberto' is in the Palazzo Conti, Padua (Mucchi and della Croce 1954, p.76n.; Donzelli and Pilo 1967, p.127).

It seems reasonable to suppose that all four paintings may have formed part of a series, although it is not possible to say whether they originated in a single commission. Celesti was working near Brescia from 1688 until 1700. A date about the middle of this period has been suggested for the Ljubljana pictures (Rizzi 1970, p.234), and Wynne has proposed a date about 1690 or shortly thereafter for No.46 (Wynne 1979).

47. Joseph and Potiphar's Wife

124.5 × 165.5 cm. (49 × 65¼ in.)

Provenance: probably Palazzo Delay (now Mafizzoli), at Toscolano near Brescia, *c.*1689; *in situ* until *c.*1974; Bonham's, London, 12 Sept. 1974 (199), where purchased.

Private collection

The wife of Potiphar, in whose house Joseph was a servant, attempted to seduce him. As he fled she took hold of his garment and later used it as evidence to her husband that Joseph had instigated the encounter (*Genesis* 39:7–20). The subject was particularly popular in the seventeenth century and was often painted as a pendant to *Susannah and the Elders*. In Venice it was treated by, among others, Padovanino (Padua), Forabosco (Rovigo), Pietro Liberi (now lost), Mazzoni, Zanchi and Carneo (all three in private collections).

Only one painting of the theme by Celesti is recorded (Mucchi and della Croce 1954). That picture was in 1954 in the saloon of the Palazzo Mafizzoli (formerly Delay) at Toscolano near Brescia, among a group of some twenty-two pictures which were probably bought from Celesti in about 1689 – the date inscribed on one of the paintings. It was described by Mucchi and della Croce (1954, p.55) as follows: 'In the "Wife of Potiphar" a noteworthy feature is the displacement of the two figures, which are perfectly linked to each other, towards the bottom of the canvas, with a freedom of composition unusual for the time. The robe of Joseph is blue with sombre tones in the areas most in shadow, while the woman is wrapped in a white shift realised through passages of grey, and holds aloft a red drape.' It would seem not unreasonable to identify No.47 with the picture so described.

The poses of both Potiphar's wife and Joseph are variations of fairly standard types. Potiphar's wife is based on the *Crouching Venus,* a model used by any number of artists, particularly for paintings of Susannah and Bathsheba, while Joseph is shown in an attitude of flight or alarm that is also quite usual. Titian in his *Diana and Actaeon* (Edinburgh), for example, used variations of both types. The boy holding the torch on the left prefigures Piazzetta and indeed in pose is markedly similar to that painter's *Standard Bearer* (Dresden).

Celesti came to Toscolano some time shortly before 1688, when he painted a number of paintings for the Duomo, including that on the high altar which is signed and dated that year. He remained in Toscolano until about 1690, and was patronised widely by the local nobility, not least the Delay family. A Count Scipione Delay is recorded as witness to Celesti's marriage in Toscolano in 1688 (Mucchi and della Croce 1954, p.17) and he may have been the patron who purchased the paintings for the Palazzo Delay. A date about 1689 seems therefore likely for the present work.

48. An Old Man holding a Pilgrim Bottle

112.5 × 91.5 cm. (44½ × 36 in.)

Provenance: recorded as having belonged to General Montbrun (d.1812), and to have come from Spain; purchased in Genoa by John Stedman, 1817; Stedman sale, Christie's, 11 July 1874 (84), bt Waters; Sir J.C. Robinson, from whom acquired by Sir Francis Cook, 1874; purchased from the Trustees of the Cook collection, 1945 (Levey 1971, No.5595).

Exhibited: Spanish Art, New Gallery, London, 1896 (151); *Spanish Painters,* Guildhall, London, 1901 (104); *Spanish Old Masters,* Grafton Galleries, London, 1913–14 (37)

Version: Harry Spiro, 1977

National Gallery

The man, who supports himself on a crutch, rests a pilgrim bottle or costrel (with loops for straps) on a globe in which is reflected a landscape with figures merrymaking before a tavern.

The picture was called *A Spanish Beggar* in the nineteenth century and bore a label on its frame inscribed 'Viva el Vino, leche de los viejos' (long live wine, milk of the aged). In the catalogue of the 1901 Guildhall exhibition the globe was interpreted as reflecting the memory of the old man who in his happy youth had also danced before the tavern; now in his old age his only source of pleasure is wine. In a general way this may be what is intended.

No.48 seems once to have been attributed to Ribera, for an old label on the back inscribed 'painted by Lo Spagnoletto' is recorded in the catalogue of the 1913–14 Grafton Galleries exhibition. It was called Velásquez by Curtis (1883, No.81) and exhibited as such in 1896 and 1901, and 'attributed to Velásquez' in 1913–14. Mayer (1911, p.137) gave it to Pablo Legote (d. *c*.1670). It was purchased as 'Spanish' and is catalogued at the National Gallery as 'Italian School, 17th(?) Century' (Levey 1971, No.5595).

Michael Levey (1971, p.146) has drawn attention to the fact that on the assumption that No.48 was by Legote, a painting of a beggar exhibited in London at Colnaghi in 1952 (*Paintings by Old Masters,* No.24), which seems almost certainly to be by the same hand, was also attributed to Legote. The Colnaghi picture was said to have been signed *'I. Bellino F',* but in fact the only letters of the signature which were distinct were *'Bell',* and a painter called I. Bellino seems never to have existed. The painter of that picture seems most likely to have been Pietro Bellotti, whose style, particularly with regard to his painting of flesh, shown wrinkled and weather-beaten, is highly distinctive, and who favoured studies of old peasant men and women.

An attribution to Bellotti for No.47 is here proposed. Comparison may be made with a signed painting by him of *Fate* in Stuttgart (Fiocco 1929/2, pl.53), a version of which is in Feltre (*Venezia* 1959, No.196).

The Feltre *Fate* is signed and dated 1654, and a date some time in the 1650s might also be reasonable for No.48.

Giovanni Antonio Fumiani *(Biography page 37)*

49. Christ disputing with the Doctors in the Temple

137.2 × 160 cm. (54 × 63 in.)

Provenance: Leonardo La Piccirella, Florence, 1959 (*Venezia* 1959, No.164); Anon. sale, Sotheby's, 17 May 1961 (133); bt Thomas Osborn Robinson, 1963; presented by him, 1968

Exhibited: Seicento a Venezia, Venice, 1959 (164)

Northampton Art Gallery

The scene is the interior of King Solomon's Temple at Jerusalem, when Mary and Joseph returned to find the twelve-year-old Christ engaged in dispute with the learned doctors (Luke, 2: 41–51). Another picture of this subject by Fumiani is in S. Aponal, Venice.

No.49 makes clear and conscious references to the High Renaissance – to Raphael and Michelangelo, and more particularly to the Venetians, Titian, Tintoretto and Veronese. The type of diagonal composition with steps and columns is found for instance in Titian's *Pesaro Madonna* and *Presentation of the Virgin*; and the dogs remind one of Veronese, as does the architecture, although it is markedly inferior and actually quite unlike Veronese's. Fumiani's treatment of the theme, however, with such prominence given to the Virgin and St Joseph, is unlike paintings of the subject by any of those artists, and in the technique his more immediate debt is to Carpioni.

A composition similar in type and size is *The Denunciation of Ananias* in the Uffizi, Florence (*Venezia* 1959, No.163). Both pictures may date from fairly late in Fumiani's career, perhaps between 1685 and 1695.

Antonio Molinari *(Biography page 40)*

146

50. The Abduction of Helen

131 × 173 cm. (51½ × 68⅛ in.)

Provenance: Lasson Gallery, London, from whom purchased, 1969

Exhibited: Lasson, London, 1969

Northampton Art Gallery

The Trojan prince Paris, in love with Helen, wife of the King of Sparta, forcibly carried her off by sea to Troy. With the Greek expedition to recover her the Trojan War began. Paris, on the right, lifts Helen into a boat which is rowed by the oarsman in the foreground.

Though a characteristic and fully acceptable painting by Molinari, the picture is not included in any of the literature on the painter.

The composition is of a type perfected by Molinari and practised also by such Venetian painters as Pietro Negri and Francesco Ruschi, wherein a group of three-quarter-length figures are presented right in the foreground, with a background composed of a glimpse of sky and some architectural detail such as the base of a column or part of an arch. Other examples by Molinari are *Esther and Ahasuerus* (private collection, Venice: Donzelli and Pilo 1967, fig.38), *Berenice* (Ringling Museum, Sarasota: Tomory 1976, fig.92), and *Sophonisba* (Zanutto collection, Venice: Martini 1964, fig.22). No.50 comes close in style to the Ringling *Berenice,* which Tomory catalogued as Lazzarini (1976, p.95), although he noted its dependence on a drawing by Molinari in Düsseldorf. Donzelli and Pilo refer to it more justifiably as Molinari.

Molinari was much influenced by Zanchi (q.v.): the placing of the figure of the oarsman in the very foreground, as well as his pose, derive directly from similar figures in Zanchi's *Abduction of Helen* (Monselice: Riccoboni 1966, fig.86) and *Agrippina saved from Shipwreck* (private collection, Lima: Riccoboni 1966, fig.87).

Compositions of this type by Molinari may be dated to the decade 1695–1705.

51. St Sebastian supported by Faith and attended by St Irene

142.2 × 132.1 cm. (56 × 52 in.)

Provenance: Rev. T.B. Murray, Lincoln's Inn Fields; presented by him, 1852

Dulwich College Art Gallery

The picture was referred to correctly as *St Sebastian with St Irene* at Dulwich until 1880, when it was called *St Sebastian with Faith and Charity* by Richter (Sparkes and Richter 1880, No.365), a title it has retained ever since. While the figure with a cross and chalice is certainly intended to represent Faith, there is no indication that the other figure is Charity, and St Irene is traditionally said to have removed the arrows from the body of St Sebastian after his attempted martyrdom (see No.31 by Renieri in this exhibition). In the bottom left part of the armour of the soldier-saint is visible. The subject was interpreted as a parallel to the Deposition of Christ – see for example No.6 here exhibited – and iconographically Bellucci's picture makes this point rather more forcibly than Renieri's.

The painting may be compared to a *Dead Christ with the Virgin and an Angel* by Veronese in the Hermitage (Pignatti 1976, fig.711). Bellucci's composition, where the figures are presented in half-length and dramatically lit, is more Baroque, but the concept behind the two pictures is the same, and Veronese also shows the fingers of the dead Christ intertwined, in his case with those of the angel. Young (1973, p.495) also suggests that the young Bellucci was inspired by Veronese, particularly for such figures as that of Faith, which appear in a number of Bellucci's early paintings.

No.51 is certainly an early work, and Young appropriately compares it with a *Roman Charity* (Young 1973, fig.2) which is signed and dated 1688.

Antonio Balestra *(Biography page 35)*

52. The Centaur Chiron receiving the Infant Achilles

106.7 × 130.8 cm. (42 × 51½ in.)

Provenance: ?purchased by George III in London *c.*1765; Buckingham House by *c.*1790–95; thence by descent (Levey 1964, No.356)

Hampton Court
Her Majesty the Queen

The sea-nymph Thetis, mother of Achilles, consigned her son to the care of the centaur Chiron who instructed him in many arts (Statius, *Achilleid,* 2:381–452).

Balestra treated the subject on at least one other occasion, in a painting described as 'un Chiron, che riceva il grande alunno da Teti, Quadro maravigliosa del Balestra', which was recorded in the Palazzo Pizzini at Rovereto in 1782 (Passamani 1962, p.178, No.9).

No.52 is one of a pair of pictures by Balestra probably purchased by George III on different occasions, with subjects drawn from the youth of Achilles. Its pendant, *Vulcan giving Thetis Armour for Achilles,* is also in the Royal Collection (Levey 1964, fig.64). Two other paintings similar in size, format and composition are at Melnik (Safarik 1964, figs.130,131); they also show Classical scenes of education of upbringing – *The Nurture of Jupiter* and *Mercury instructing Cupid* (called erroneously by Safarik *Mercury and Diana*).

The Melnik pictures have been dated to the artist's maturity rather than his old age, i.e. 1710–25 (Safarik 1964, p.115). No.52 would seem stylistically earlier, and Michael Levey has compared it and its pendant with two *Allegories* at Pommersfelden (Battisti 1954, pl.xii, fig.12), which he believes to have been commissioned *c.*1715.

53. Bacchus and Ariadne

75.9 × 63.2 cm. (29⅞ × 24⅞ in.)

Provenance: Sir Robert Peel (d.1850); purchased with the Peel collection, 1871 (Levey 1971, No.851)

Exhibited: The National Gallery lends: Pictures from Eighteenth-Century Venice, Bristol City Art Gallery, Norwich Castle Museum and Wolverhampton Central Art Gallery, 1976–77 (10).

Version: private coll., Italy (Daniels 1976/2, fig.303/1)

National Gallery

Ariadne was abandoned on the island of Naxos by Theseus and there discovered by the god Bacchus. Their meeting, with Bacchus rose-crowned as here, is described in Philostratus' *Imagines* (1:15). Cupids descending bear a hymeneal torch celebrating the union of Bacchus and Ariadne. The subject, which was once referred to as *Venus Sleeping,* was identified by Michael Levey (Levey 1971, p.195).

The picture was purchased as Ricci and its attribution has never been and need not be doubted. Ricci treated the subject on at least nine other occasions. Of these works, No.53 comes closest in composition to two, that sold at Christie's on 1 May 1959 (70) (Daniels 1976/2, fig.243), and that in the Palazzo Taverna at Monte Giordano (Daniels 1976/2, fig.381). The version of the present composition (see *Version*) is slightly larger and differs mainly in that Ariadne and the bacchante who attends her are more modestly dressed. As pointed out by Martini (1964, p.161, fig.53), No.53 derives closely from a painting of the same subject by Carpioni (q.v.).

Bacchus and Ariadne is certainly a fairly early work: a date about 1705 was proposed by Michael Levey (1971, p.196), and it has not been disputed by Daniels.

54. Rebecca at the Well

127.3 × 104.5 cm. (50⅛ × 41⅛ in.)

Provenance: Claude D. Rotch 1951; bequeathed by him, 1962 (Levey 1971, No.6332)

Exhibited: Eighteenth-Century Venice, Whitechapel Art Gallery, London, 1951 (80); *Italian Art and Britain,* R.A., London, 1960 (193)

National Gallery

Abraham sent his servant Eliezer into Mesopotamia to seek a bride for his son Isaac. Eliezer stopped by a well and prayed that the woman who would give him and his camels a drink from the well would be a suitable bride for Isaac. When Rebecca came, she gave him and his camels water, and Eliezer gave her a golden earring and two gold bracelets. (Genesis, 24)

The theme, which was treated by Veronese (Washington), enjoyed some popularity with Venetian painters of the seventeenth century, and was painted by, among others, Mazzoni (Hermitage, Leningrad), Carpioni (in two pictures now lost), Celesti (Faenza), Bellucci (Pommersfelden), Lazzarini (Ca' Correr, Venice), Piazzetta (Brera, Milan), and Sebastiano Ricci (in at least four pictures: Daniels 1976/2, Nos. 83,418,479,480). Most of these pictures are broader in composition than No.54, with many more figures and in full-length.

Pellegrini painted the same subject on at least two other occasions – in a picture formerly in Washington (now destroyed: Levey 1959/2, fig.7) and in one in Potsdam. What is conceivably a third representation of the theme by Pellegrini is a drawing at Düsseldorf called *Episode from the Life of a Saint* (Bettagno 1959, No.34). No.54 is a simpler composition than the ex-Washington picture, and the relation between Rebecca and Eliezer is made more forceful. A painting by Ricci of the same subject in Parma (Daniels 1976/2, No.418), of about 1724, shows both Rebecca and Eliezer in poses similar to those seen here.

No.54 is generally dated to Pellegrini's English period, between 1708 and 1713, and Young (1969, p.196) places it early in that time, before 1711.

Bibliography of literature cited in the text

The arrangement is chronological and then, within each year, alphabetical by author or key name. Page references are to the beginning of an article.

For complete bibliographies of Venetian seventeenth-century painting see the following:

La pittura del Seicento a Venezia, exhibition cat. (Venice, 1959)

C. Donzelli and G. M. Pilo, *I pittori del Seicento veneto* (Florence, 1967)

An up-to-date complete bibliography will be included in Professor Rodolfo Pallucchini's *La pittura veneziana del Seicento,* to be published in 1980

Mancini 1617   G. Mancini, *Considerazione sulla pittura* (1617–c.1621; ed. A. Marucchi and L. Salerno, Rome, 1956–57)

Totti 1638   P. Totti, *Ritratto di Roma moderna* (Rome, 1638)

Ridolfi 1648   C. Ridolfi, *Le maraviglie dell'arte, etc.* (Venice, 1648; references are to the ed. by D. von Hadeln, Berlin, 1914–24)

Boschini 1660   M. Boschini, *La carta del navegar pitoresco* (Venice, 1660; ed. A. Pallucchini, Venice and Rome, 1966)

Boschini 1664   M. Boschini, *Le minere della pittura* (Venice, 1664)

Boschini 1674   M. Boschini, *Le ricche minere della pittura veneziana* (Venice, 1674)

Soprani 1674   R. Soprani, *Vite de' pittori, scultori et architetti genovesi . . .* (Genoa, 1674)

Sandrart 1675   J. von Sandrart, *Teutsche Academie* (1675; ed. A. R. Peltzer, Munich, 1925)

Passeri 1675–79   G. B. Passeri, *Vite de pittori, scultori et architetti* (1677–79; ed J. Hess as *Die Künstlerbiographien von Giovanni Battista Passeri,* Leipzig and Vienna, 1934)

Sandrart 1683   J. von Sandrart, *Academia nobilissimae artis pictoriae* (Nuremberg, 1683)

Orlandi 1704   P. A. Orlandi, *Abecedario pittorico* (Bologna, 1704)

Dal Pozzo 1718   B. Dal Pozzo, *Le vite de' pittori, degli scultori et architetti veronesi* (Verona, 1718)

Pascoli 1736   L. Pascoli, *Vite de' pittori, scultori ed architetti moderni* (Rome, 1730–36)

Temanza 1738   T. Temanza, *Zibaldon di memorie storiche appartenente a professori delle arti del disegno* (ms., 1738, in Bibl. Seminario Patriarcale, Venice)

Raccolta 1743   Pietro Monaco, *Raccolta di 55 istorie sacre* (Venice, 1743)

Ratti 1769   C. G. Ratti, *Delle vite de' pittori, scultori ed architetti genovesi . . . in continuazione dell'opera di Raffaelle Soprani* (Genoa, 1769)

Zanetti 1771   A. M. Zanetti, *Della pittura veneziana* (Venice, 1771)

Arnaldi 1779   E. Arnaldi, *Descrizione delle architetture, pitture e scolture di Vicenza* (Vicenza, 1779)

Rossetti 1780   G. Rossetti, *Descrizione delle pitture, sculture ed architetture di Padova* (Padua, 1780)

Lanzi 1789   see Lanzi 1822

Burghley 1797   *A History or Description of Burghley House* (Shrewsbury, 1797)

Moschini 1817   G. A. Moschini, *Guida per la città di Padova all'amico delle belle arti* (Venice, 1817)

Lanzi 1822   L. Lanzi, *Storia pittorica della Italia,* 6 vol. (Florence, 1822; later ed. of work first publ. Bassano, 1789)

Buchanan 1824   W. Buchanan, *Memoirs of Painting* (London, 1824)

Cicogna 1853   E. Cicogna, *Delle iscrizioni veneziane* (Venice, 1824–53)

Waagen 1854   G. Waagen, *Treasures of Art in Great Britain,* 3 vol. (London, 1854)

Manfrin 1856   Catalogo dei quadri nella Galleria Manfrin in Venezia (1856)

Waagen 1857   G. Waagen, *Galleries and Cabinets of Art in Great Britain* (London, 1857)

Manfrin 1872   G. Nicoletti, *Pinacoteca Manfrin a Venezia* (Venice, 1872)

Crowe and Cavalcaselle 1877   J. A. Crowe and G. B. Cavalcaselle, *Titian* (London, 1877)

Stephens 1877   F. G. Stephens, *On the Pictures at Cobham Hall* (London, 1877)

Sparkes and Richter 1880   J. Sparkes and J. Richter, *Catalogue of Pictures in the Dulwich College Gallery* (London, 1880)

Curtis 1883   C. B. Curtis, *Velasquez and Murillo* (London, 1883)

Zannandreis 1891   D. Zannandreis, *Le vite dei pittori, scultori e architetti veronese* (Verona, 1891)

Holborn 1903   J. B. S. Holborn, *Tintoretto* (1903)

Powerscourt 1903   Viscount Powerscourt, *A Description and History of Powerscourt* (London, 1903)

Davies 1907   R. Davies, 'An inventory of the Duke of Buckingham's pictures . . . at York House in 1635', *Burlington Magazine,* 1907, p.376

Trench 1910   R. C. Trench, *Notes on the Parables of Our Lord* (London, 1910)

Mayer 1911   A. L. Mayer, *Die Sevillaner Malerschule* (Leipzig, 1911)

Collins Baker 1912   C. H. Collins Baker, 'A Palma Giovane in the National Gallery?', *Burlington Magazine,* 1912, p.234

Hadeln 1913   D. von Hadeln, 'Damiano Mazza', *Zeitschrift für Bildende Kunst,* 1913, p.249

Oldenbourg 1914   R. Oldenbourg, 'Jan Lys', *Jahrbuch der Königlich Preussischen Kunstsammlungen,* 1914, p.136

Borenius 1916   T. Borenius, *Pictures by the Old Masters in the Library of Christ Church, Oxford* (Oxford, 1916)

Strickland 1916   W. G. Strickland, *A Descriptive Catalogue of the Pictures, Busts, Statues in Trinity College, Dublin* (Dublin, 1916)

Hervey 1921   M. F. S. Hervey, *The Life of . . . Thomas Howard Earl of Arundel* (1921)

Marangoni 1922–23   M. Marangoni, 'Domenico Feti', *Dedalo,* 1922–23, p.695

Voss 1924   H. Voss, 'Die caravaggeske Frühzeit von Simon Vouet und Nicolas Regnier', *Zeitschrift für Bildende Kunst,* 1924

Longhi 1926   R. Longhi, 'Il trio dei veronesi: Bassetti, Turchi, Ottino', *Vita artistica,* 1926, I, p.123

Walpole 1927–28   P. Toynbee, ed., 'Horace Walpole's Journals of Visits to Country Seats, etc.', *Walpole Society,* XVI, 1927–28, p.9

Pevsner 1928   N. Pevsner, *Barockmalerei in den Romanischen Ländern* (Potsdam, 1928)

Delogu 1929   G. Delogu, 'Pittori genovesi del '600', *L'Arte,* 1929, p.172

Fiocco 1929/1   G. Fiocco, 'Sebastiano Mazzoni', *Dedalo,* 1928–29, p.290

Fiocco 1929/2   G. Fiocco, *Venetian Painting of the Seicento and the Settecento* (Florence, 1929)

Ivanoff 1936   N. Ivanoff, 'Appunti su Francesco Maffei', *Rivista d'Arte,* 1936, p.398

Steinbart 1940   K. Steinbart, *Johann Liss, der Maler aus Hollstein* (Berlin, 1940)

Hoogewerff 1941–42   G. J. Hoogewerff, *De Noord-Nederlandsche Schilderkunst,* 1, IV (The Hague, 1941–42)

Borenius 1943   T. Borenius, 'Sir Peter Lely's collection', *Burlington Magazine,* 1943, p.185

Ivanoff 1944–45   N. Ivanoff, 'Il grottesco nella pittura veneziana del '600: Pietro Vecchia', *Emporium,* 1944–45, p.85

Tietze-Conrat 1945   E. Tietze-Conrat, 'The Wemyss Allegory in the Art Institute of Chicago', *Art Bulletin,* 1945, p.268

Longhi 1946   R. Longhi, *Viatico per cinque secoli di pittura veneziana* (Florence, 1946)

Steinbart 1946   K. Steinbart, *Johann Liss* (Vienna, 1946)

Bertini 1949   A. Bertini, 'Una parabola del Fetti ritrovata', *Emporium,* 1949, p.25

Popham and Wilde 1949   A. E. Popham and J. Wilde, *Italian Drawings of the XV and XVI Centuries in the Collection of His Majesty the King at Windsor Castle* (London, 1949)

Bloch 1950   V. Bloch, 'Liss and his *Fall of Phaeton*', *Burlington Magazine,* 1950, p.278

Fröhlich-Bume 1952   L. Fröhlich-Bume, 'Su Pietro Vecchia', *Paragone,* 1952, no.31, p.34

Waterhouse 1952   E. K. Waterhouse, 'Paintings from Venice for seventeenth-century England: some records of a forgotten transaction', *Italian Studies,* 1952, p.1

Battisti 1954   E. Battisti, 'Antonio Balestra', *Commentari,* 1954, p.26

Exeter 1954   The Marchioness of Exeter, *Catalogue of Pictures at Burghley House, Northamptonshire* (unpublished ms., 1954)

Ivanoff 1954   N. Ivanoff, 'I ritratti dell'Avogaria', *Arte Veneta,* 1954, p.272

Mucchi and della Croce 1954   A. M. Mucchi and C. della Croce, *Il pittore Andrea Celesti* (Milan, 1954)

Michelini 1955   P. Michelini, 'Domenico Fetti a Venezia', *Arte Veneta,* 1955, p.123

Wildenstein 1955   *Artists in 17th-Century Rome,* exhibition cat. (Wildenstein, London, 1955)

Arslan 1956   E. Arslan, *Vicenza I, Le chiese* (Rome, 1956)

Ivanoff 1956   N. Ivanoff, *Catalogo della Mostra di F. Maffei* (Venice, 1956)

Matteucci 1956   A. M. Matteucci, 'Note all'attività genovese di B. Strozzi', *Emporium,* 1956, p.195

Paccagnini 1956   G. Paccagnini, 'Dipinti di Domenico Feti a Mantova', *La Critica d'Arte,* 1956, p.578

Fenyo 1958   I. Fenyo, 'Contributo di rapporti artistici tra Palma Giovane e Bernardo Strozzi', *Acta Historiae Artium Academiae Scientiarum Hungariae,* 1958, p.143

Ivanoff 1958   N. Ivanoff, 'Sebastiano Mazzoni', *Saggi e Memorie di Storia dell'Arte*, 1958, p.209

Laclotte 1958   M. Laclotte, 'Le "Bon Samaritain" de Langetti', *Bull. des Musées lyonnais*, 1958, p.1

Millar 1958   O. Millar, 'Abraham van der Doort's Catalogue of the Collections of Charles I', *Walpole Society*, XXXVII, 1958–60

Steinbart 1958–59   K. Steinbart, 'Das Werk des Johann Liss in alter und neuer Sicht', *Saggi e Memorie di Storia dell'Arte*, 1958–59, p.157

Bettagno 1959   A. Bettagno, *Disegni e dipinti di Giovanni Antonio Pellegrini*, exhibition cat. (Venice, 1959)

Ivanoff 1959   N. Ivanoff, 'Mostra della pittura del Seicento a Venezia', *Il Verri*, 1959

Levey 1959/1   M. Levey, *National Gallery Catalogues: The German School* (London, 1959)

Levey 1959/2   M. Levey, *Painting in XVIII Century Venice* (London, 1959)

Venezia 1959   La pittura del Seicento a Venezia, exhibition cat. (Ca'Pesaro, Venice, 1959)

Birmingham 1960   *Catalogue of Paintings, City Museum and Art Gallery, Birmingham* (Birmingham, 1960)

Salerno 1960   L. Salerno, 'The Picture Gallery of Vincenzo Giustiniani', *Burlington Magazine*, 1960, pp.21, 93, 135

Waterhouse 1960   E. K. Waterhouse, 'A Note on British collecting of Italian pictures in the later seventeenth century', *Burlington Magazine*, 1960, p.54

Ewald 1960–61   G. Ewald, 'Inediti di Sebastiano Mazzoni', *Acropoli*, 1960–61, p.187

Ashmolean 1961   *Catalogue of Paintings in the Ashmolean Museum* (Oxford, 1961)

Askew 1961   P. Askew, 'The Parable Paintings of Domenico Fetti', *Art Bulletin*, 1961, p.21

Fomiciova 1961   T. Fomiciova, 'La pittura veneta del Seicento nell'Ermitage e negli altri musei dell'U.R.S.S.', *Arte Veneta*, 1961, p.133

Hoff 1961   U. Hoff, *European Painting and Sculpture before 1800* (National Gallery of Victoria, Melbourne, 1961)

Pilo 1961/1   G. M. Pilo, 'La pala per S. Pietro Martire di Padova ed altri inediti di Francesco Maffei', *Arte antica e moderna – Studi in onore di Roberto Longhi* (Venice, 1961), p.390

Pilo 1961/2   G. M. Pilo, *Carpioni* (Venice, 1961)

York 1961   *Catalogue of Paintings, City of York Art Gallery*, 3 vol. (York, 1961)

Riccoboni 1961–62   A. Riccoboni, 'Antonio Zanchi', *Acropoli*, 1961–62, p.5

Barbieri 1962   F. Barbieri, *Il Museo Civico di Vicenza – Dipinti e sculture dal XVI al XVIII secolo* (Venice, 1962)

Mortari 1962   L. Mortari, 'Aggiunte allo Strozzi', *Paragone*, 1962, no.153, p.26

Pallucchini 1962   R. Pallucchini, 'Contributi alla pittura veneziana del Seicento: il viaggio a Roma del Padovanino', *Arte Veneta*, 1962, pp.121, 137

Passamani 1962   B. Passamani, 'Aggiunte ad Antonio Balestra', *Arte Veneta*, 1962, p.177

Ivanoff 1963   N. Ivanoff, 'A bozzetto by Domenico Fetti', *Connoisseur*, Sept. 1963, p.38

Finch 1964   *Venetian Baroque Paintings*, exhibition cat. (Finch College Museum of Art, New York, 1964)

Gore 1964   St J. Gore, *Polesden Lacey* (The National Trust, 1964)

Levey 1964   M. Levey, *The Later Italian Pictures in the Collection of Her Majesty the Queen* (London, 1964)

Martini 1964   E. Martini, *La pittura veneziana del Settecento* (Venice, 1964)

Safarik 1964   E. A. Safarik, 'Il Settecento veneziano nelle collezioni cecoslovacche', *Arte Veneta*, 1964, p.110

Ewald 1965   G. Ewald, *Johann Carl Loth, 1632–1698* (Amsterdam, 1965)

Garlick 1965   K. Garlick, 'Pictures at Weston Park, Staffordshire', *Country Life*, 1965, pp.1134, 1210

Ivanoff 1965/1   N. Ivanoff, 'Nicolas Regnier', *Arte antica e moderna*, 1965, p.12

Ivanoff 1965/2   N. Ivanoff, 'Gian Francesco Loredan e l'ambiente artistico a Venezia nel Seicento', *Ateneo Veneto*, 1965, p.186

Savini-Branca 1965   S. Savini-Branca, *Il collezionismo veneziano nel '600* (Padua, 1965)

Clark 1966   K. Clark, *Rembrandt and the Italian Renaissance* (London, 1966)

Ferrari and Scavizzi 1966   O. Ferrari and G. Scavizzi, *Luca Giordano*, 3 vol. (1966)

Mortari 1966   L. Mortari, *Bernardo Strozzi* (Rome, 1966)

Riccoboni 1966   A. Riccoboni, 'Antonio Zanchi e la pittura veneziana del Seicento', *Saggi e Memorie di Storia dell'Arte*, v, 1966, p.53

Stefani 1966   M. Stefani, 'Nuovi contributi alla conoscenza di Giambattista Langetti', *Arte Veneta*, 1966, p.190

Byam Shaw 1967   J. Byam Shaw, *Paintings by Old Masters at Christ Church, Oxford* (London, 1967)

Donzelli and Pilo 1967   C. Donzelli and G. M. Pilo, *I pittori del Seicento veneto* (Florence, 1967)

Hull 1967   *Venetian Baroque and Rococo*, exhibition cat. (Ferens Art Gallery, Kingston upon Hull, 1967)

Moir 1967   A. Moir, *The Italian Followers of Caravaggio,* 2 vol. (Cambridge, Mass., 1967)

Ottani Cavina 1968   A. Ottani Cavina, *Carlo Saraceni* (Milan, 1968)

Pevsner 1969   N. Pevsner, *South Lancashire,* The Buildings of England (Harmondsworth, 1969)

Pallucchini 1969   R. Pallucchini, *Titian,* 2 vol. (Florence, 1969)

Young 1969   E. Young, 'More about Pellegrini's Methods and Development', *Apollo,* 1969, p.194

Rizzi 1970   A. Rizzi, 'Dipinti di Andrea Celesti e Pietro Ricchi a Lubiana', *Arte Veneta,* 1970, p.233

Urbino 1970   *Mostra di opere d'arte restaurate* (Palazzo Ducale, Urbino, 1970)

Levey 1971   M. Levey, *National Gallery Catalogues: The Seventeenth and Eighteenth Century Italian Schools* (London, 1971)

Macandrew 1971   H. Macandrew, 'A silver basin designed by Strozzi', *Burlington Magazine,* 1971, p.4

Perina 1971   C. T. Perina, 'Precisazione sul Fetti', *Antichità Viva,* 1971, p.10

Riccoboni 1971   A. Riccoboni, 'Novità Zanchiane', in *Studi . . . in onore di Antonio Morassi* (Venice, 1971), p.262

Sagep 1971   *La pittura a Genova e in Liguria dal Seicento al primo Novecento* (Genoa, 1971)

Antonov 1972   V. Antonov, 'Aggiunte allo Strozzi', *Antichità Viva,* 1972, p.18

Fantelli 1972   P. L. Fantelli, 'Su Niccolò Renieri ritrattista', *Atti dell'Istituto Veneto,* 1972–73

Newcome 1972   M. Newcome, *Genoese Baroque Drawings,* exhibition cat. (University Art Gallery, Binghamton, N.Y., 1972)

Rinaldi 1973   S. M. Rinaldi, 'Il libro dei disegni di Palma il Giovane del British Museum', *Arte Veneta,* 1973, p.125

Young 1973   E. Young, 'Antonio Bellucci in England and elsewhere', *Apollo,* 1973, p.492

Fantelli 1974/1   P. L. Fantelli, 'Niccolò Renieri, pittor fiamengo', *Saggi e Memorie di Storia dell'Arte,* IX, 1974, p.77

Fantelli 1974/2   P. L. Fantelli, 'Le figlie di Niccolò Renieri: un saggio attributivo', *Arte Veneta,* XXVIII, 1974, p.267

Ottani Cavina 1974   A. Ottani Cavina, 'Marcantonio Bassetti', in *Cinquant'anni di pittura veronese 1580–1630,* exhibition cat. (Verona, 1974)

Pigler 1974   A. Pigler, *Barockthemen,* 3 vol. (Budapest, 1974)

Scaglietti 1974   D. Scaglietti, 'Alessandro Turchi', in *Cinquant'anni di pittura veronese 1580–1630,* exhibition cat. (Verona, 1974)

Valentin et al. 1974   *Valentin et les Caravagesques français,* exhibition cat. (Grand Palais, Paris, 1974)

Garlick 1974–76   K. Garlick, 'A Catalogue of the Pictures at Althorp', *Walpole Society,* XLV, 1974–76

Gould 1975   C. Gould, *National Gallery Catalogues: The Sixteenth Century Italian Schools* (London, 1975)

Lavin 1975   M. A. Lavin, *Seventeenth Century Barberini Documents and Inventories of Art* (New York, 1975)

Wethey 1975   H. Wethey, *The Paintings of Titian,* III (London, 1975)

Liss 1975–76   Johann Liss, exhibition cat. (Rathaus, Augsburg, and Cleveland Museum of Art, 1975–76)

Askew 1976   P. Askew, 'Domenico Fetti's use of prints: three instances', in *Tribute to Wolfgang Stechow: Print Review,* no.5 (New York, 1976), p.14

Daniels 1976/1   J. Daniels, *Sebastiano Ricci* (Hove, 1976)

Daniels 1976/2   J. Daniels, *L'opera completa di Sebastiano Ricci* (Milan, 1976)

Pignatti 1976   T. Pignatti, *Veronese,* 2 vol. (Venice, 1976)

Tomory 1976   P. Tomory, *Catalogue of the Italian Paintings before 1800: The John and Mable Ringling Museum of Art* (Sarasota, Fla., 1976)

Wright 1976   C. Wright, *Old Master Paintings in Britain* (London, 1976)

Fantelli 1977   P. L. Fantelli, 'Notarella sul Seicento veneto', in *Per Maria Cionini Visani* (Padua, 1977), p.105

Wynne 1977   M. Wynne, 'Fesch paintings in the National Gallery of Ireland', *Gazette des beaux-arts,* Jan. 1977, p.1

Askew 1978   P. Askew, 'Fetti's Portrait of an Actor reconsidered', *Burlington Magazine,* 1978, p.59

Fletcher 1979   J. Fletcher, 'Marco Boschini and Paolo del Sera, collectors and connoisseurs of Venice', *Apollo,* Nov. 1979

Knox 1979   G. Knox, 'Pagani, Pellegrini and Piazzetta at "The Elms"', *Apollo,* Nov. 1979

Potterton 1979/1   H. Potterton, 'A Saraceni for the National Gallery', *Burlington Magazine,* Jan. 1979, p.28

Potterton 1979/2   H. Potterton, 'Aspects of Venetian Seventeenth-Century Painting', *Apollo,* Nov. 1979

Rinaldi 1979   S. M. Rinaldi, 'Paintings by Palma Il Giovane in Great Britain', *Apollo,* Nov. 1979

Wynne 1979   M. Wynne, 'A portrait by Andrea Celesti', *Burlington Magazine,* Sept. 1979

Index of Exhibited Artists

Figures in **bold** type refer to bibliographies and catalogue entries

Printed in England for the Trustees by
Staples Printers Kettering Limited, The George Press, Kettering Northamptonshire